C000257681

# Field Safety in Uncontrolled Environments: A Process-Based Guidebook


*By*
Stephen R. Oliveri
Kevin Bohacs



Published by

**The American Association of Petroleum Geologists**
Tulsa, Oklahoma
*and*
**The Division of Environmental Geosciences**
Tulsa, Oklahoma
*and*
**ExxonMobil Upstream Geoscience**
Houston, Texas

ISBN: 0-89181-827-8



AAPG Editor: Ernest A. Mancini
AAPG Geoscience Director: James B. Blankenship
DEG President: Steven P. Tischer
DEG Editor: Gerald R. Baum
ExxonMobil Upstream Research Company Vice President of Geoscience: Anne Reeckmann
ExxonMobil Exploration Company Vice President: Mark A. Solien

This publication is available from:

The AAPG Bookstore
P.O. Box 979
Tulsa, OK U.S.A. 74101-0979
Phone: 1-918-584-2555
or 1-800-364-AAPG (U.S.A. only)
Fax: 1-918-260-2652
or 1-800-898-2274 (U.S.A. only)
E-mail: bookstore@aapg.org
www.aapg.org

Geological Society Publishing House
Unit 7, Brassmill Enterprise Centre
Brassmill Lane, Bath BA13JN
U.K.
Phone: +44-1225-445046
Fax: +44-1225-442836
E-mail: sales@geolsoc.org.uk
www.geolsoc.org.uk

Canadian Society of Petroleum Geologists
No. 160, 540 Fifth Avenue S.W.
Calgary, Alberta T2P 0M2
Canada
Phone: 1-403-264-5610
Fax: 1-403-264-5898
E-mail: Jaime.croft@cspg.org
www.cspg.org

Affiliated East-West Press Private Ltd.
G-1/16 Ansari Road, Darya Ganj
New Delhi 110 002
India
Phone: +91-11-23279113
Fax: +91-11-23260538
E-mail: affiliat@vsnl.com

# Table of Contents

# About the Authors

***Stephen R. Oliveri*** is a safety and risk management professional who has been instrumental in the development of safety and operations integrity systems worldwide. He has worked as a safety, field safety, and operations professional for 30 years in the oil industry. He has been a teacher, scoutmaster, coach, and official at various stages of his life and continues to participate in a variety of safety and health-related activities. He has been on the board of directors for Texas youth sports and is currently the vice president of the Texas Association of Sports Officials (TASO)—Rice Belt Chapter.

Oliveri joined Exxon Production Research Company in 1985 after nine successful years of field exploration with Gulf Oil Corporation. He has managed field operations in more than eight foreign countries and has developed safety manuals for both laboratories and field programs. He has received numerous safety leadership awards, chaired safety and operations integrity evaluation teams, and is a consultant for a variety of safety and risk assessment programs.

***Kevin Bohacs*** is a sedimentologist and stratigrapher who has taught first aid and field operations safety for more than 35 years. He has been an American Red Cross Instructor, trainer in emergency response, and CPR/AED trainer for more than 25 years. He is an Eagle Scout and an assistant scoutmaster. He has worked and volunteered as a fire fighter, paramedic, lifeguard, water safety instructor, and camp director.

Bohacs was graduated from the University of Connecticut with a B.Sc. (honors) in Geology and earned a Sc.D. in Experimental Sedimentology from M.I.T. He joined Exxon Production Research Company in 1981 and has conducted fieldwork and training on six continents and in more than twenty countries. He has received numerous outstanding instructor awards and is a fellow of the Geological Society of America and a national fellow of the Explorers Club.

His wife, Susan Mitterling, works with him on many training and testing exercises—and always comes up with the most challenging mock disaster scenarios.

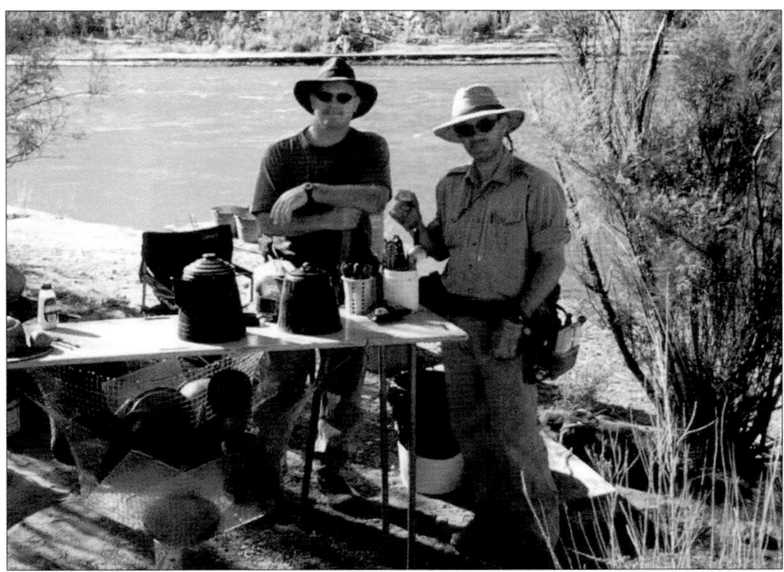

# Acknowledgments

This work is the outgrowth of many years of fieldwork, operations planning, risk assessment, and safety programs—indeed, the entire safety culture of ExxonMobil.

Many people have supported us in these efforts and we thank them all. Those who helped us specifically with this publication include our fellow members of the Field Safety Steering Committee: Mark Bixby, Jim Detamore, Jeff Thomas, and Rick Winters; the Field Safety Steering Committee: Kevin Barnes, Tom Bultman, Jim Detamore, Tim Fischer, Susan Hippler, Larry Karasevich, Glenn Landry, Mike McGroder, Chris Tenney, and Fred Zelt, along with Cathy Simmons, URC nurse; Deena Buford, M.D.; Sid Chalka (EMEC SHE), Bette Hillman (EMURC SHE), Don Gilbert (EMEC SHE), Nick Worontsoff (Central SHE), and Kristy Vandenberg (American Red Cross).

Patti Bourland, Gregory Davis, Lincoln Foreman, Clem Harrell, Jeff Hartley, John Leiphart, Jim Markello, John McPherson, Penny Patterson, Dave Reynolds, Sally Rigg, Jim Schriver, and Ryan Tisdale provided helpful suggestions, feedback, and the stimulating discussions necessary to establish a sound safety and risk framework.

We also acknowledge the unwavering management support of Steve Cassiani, Anne Reeckmann, Mark Solien, Carlos Dengo, Fred Zelt, Larry Baker, Ray Charles, Elijah White, Larry Karasevich, Ian Russell, Mark Richardson, and Gary Isaksen.

This truly was a team effort and we appreciate all of the assistance.

# Dedications

*Stephen R. Oliveri*

To my parents Anthony and Patricia Oliveri, who instilled in me a passion for knowledge and the desire to protect my fellow man and the surrounding environment. These values have proved to be the driving force behind the science of field safety;

To Jody Murello, who introduced me to the wonderful world of geology and taught me to work hard and observe my surroundings;

And to my wife, Linda, whose undying support has inspired me to new heights.

*Kevin Bohacs*

To Dr. Richard O'Leary, who taught me how to provide first aid in the great north woods;

To Lloyd Duff, who taught me how to teach first aid in the great north woods;

To Blair Sutherland, David Sutherland, James Russell, Gary Schmitz, and Ross Ogden, with whom I taught first aid over the years;

And to my wife, Susan, whom I met teaching first aid, and whom made it all worthwhile.

# Field Safety in Uncontrolled Environments
## A Process-Based Guidebook

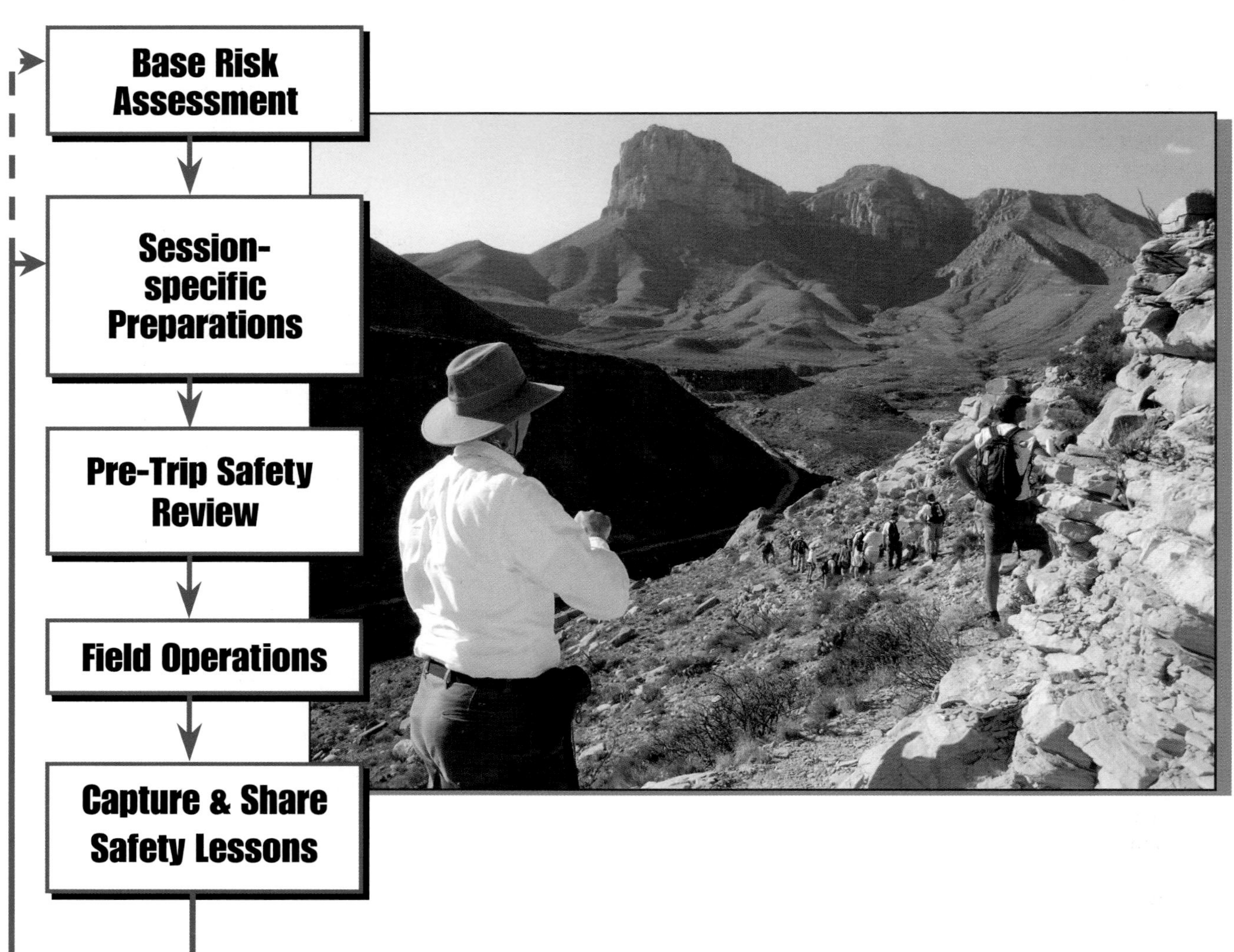

# Preface

Field activities are normally safe (typically safer than home), but accidents do happen, and when they happen, it can be devastating.

Consequences are potentially so serious that we must do something about it, and we can take measures to reduce the risk of a serious accident significantly. It is, however, difficult sometimes to get excited about safety preparations and prevention—in many ways it is like buying insurance: we know we need to have it, but we hope that we never need to use it. Similarly with field safety preparations, it may be hard to be motivated about something you never want to use. But also like insurance, for a relatively small investment beforehand, we can reap great benefits later.

We have found many other benefits from systematically addressing field safety issues: it makes fieldwork and schools more effective by sharpening the focus on the key technical and learning objectives. It builds the confidence of new instructors and trip leaders. Field experiences are more rewarding for students who can focus on observation and learning. It heightens safety awareness in everyday life. Fieldwork goes more smoothly and efficiently from pre-trip thought, discussions, planning, and preparation.

The field safety preparations take some time initially, but become low maintenance for subsequent sessions. As it is practiced, the process becomes almost second nature and part of the normal course of doing business—like packing lunches for the field or filling vehicles with fuel.

Ultimately, field safety is the right thing to do, ethically, technically, and financially. "No technical/ business objective is so important that it will be pursued through the sacrifice of safety" is a prime tenet of ExxonMobil's (and many other companies') safety programs. Nothing is more precious and irreplaceable than life—all other considerations are secondary. Additionally, safe operations are technically sound because no learning or scientific advance will occur if someone gets hurt. Accidents may jeopardize an entire scientific or academic program and have resulted in loss of access to numerous important field sites. Safety also makes good financial sense because organizations have a lot invested in their members. Their training, experience, productivity, and potential are all valuable assets that can be lost through unsafe conduct. Academic organizations literally are investing in the future of our science through their students. Accidents threaten these investments and it is financially sound to expend time and money to protect them. Hence, an effective safety program is important for our people, our organizations, and our science.

The field safety program elaborated in this manual is straightforward, widely applicable, and scaleable to the wide range of field activities, from short roadside stops to month-long backcountry expeditions. Its 5 steps apply to all field activities, identifying the roles and responsibilities that must be addressed in pre-trip preparations, field operations, and post-trip follow-up. The level of detailed effort required, however, is dictated by the level of hazards that might be encountered and the size of the group participating (leading groups of more than 5 or so people requires different approaches than being in the field with only yourself and a partner). For example, a typical one-week field school in the western U.S.A. takes about 16 hours of preparation time at first, and then about 4 hours preparation for subsequent sessions. For a week of fieldwork, the safety preparations take about 4 hours for the first visit, and then less than 2 hours for successive visits.

Pre-trip preparations begin with identifying hazards that might be encountered and assessing their risks. This information is shared with all participants and used to plan prevention, mitigation, and emergency-response measures. These measures include obtaining safety equipment and supplies, identifying emergency response resources for each field location, and training participants in defensive driving, first aid, and other safety courses as needed. Simple preparations such as having the right phone number to call save valuable time in case of an emergency.

In the field, all trips begin with a short briefing that covers the technical and learning objectives of the activity, as well as general safety information (such as what each participant is to do in case of an accident). More specific safety briefings are given at the start of each day and at each field stop (these last less than 5 minutes). For field stops, there are specific standard operating procedures for "normal" activities (hiking, boating, and swimming) that provide strategies for control of the group, avoiding hazards, and monitoring for unsafe behavior. A designated participant records field experiences and safety recommendations in a Safety Log. In case of injury or serious illness, an emergency response plan names who will provide first aid, call for help, and take charge of the rest of the group.

Post-trip follow-up draws upon the Safety Log to capture safety lessons learned in the field and shares them with other groups as well as fine tune plans for future activities. This feedback loop enhances and upgrades safe operations continuously based on local experience and conditions. Such customization makes it easier for an organization to make safety an integral part of their basic conduct.

We hope that your organization will adopt some version of this program and have written this manual both as an overview of the process and as a template for your own program. We have included digital versions of the checklists and forms so that you can customize them easily for your organization. We must emphasize, though, that developing an effective field safety program requires more than inserting your organization's name on the forms—the discussions, debates, and research that go into customizing the methodology and making it part of your organization's culture are far more important than anything written down on paper. Such efforts are well rewarded in a higher level of confidence and safety in field operations. We wish you the best in your safety endeavors.

# 1 Overview

Overview

Risk Assessment Process

↓

Planning and Preparation

↓

Pre-Activity Safety Review

↓

Field Operations

↓

Post-Activity Learning

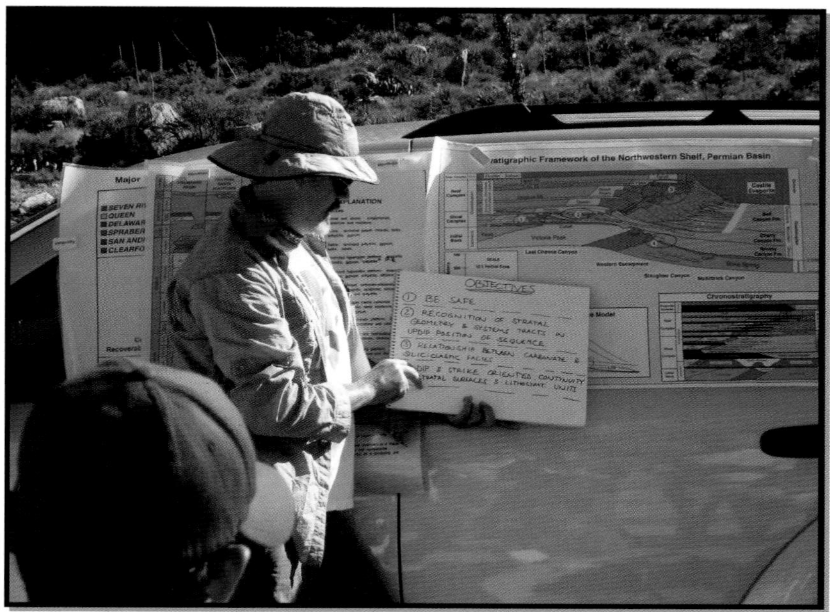

*"Adventures, of course, are always associated with exploration. Yet they are the one thing which a real explorer tries to guard against. My favorite quotation is Stefansson's dicutm: 'Adventures are a mark of incompetence.' It says so much in a very few words. It means that if you have an adventurous expedition you did not prepare yourself adequately. Adventures are a nuisance. They interface with work... If the explorer has a clear-cut problem to solve and an honest desire to do something really worthwhile he will prepare against adventures."*

*Roy Chapman Andrews, 1935, This Business of Exploring*

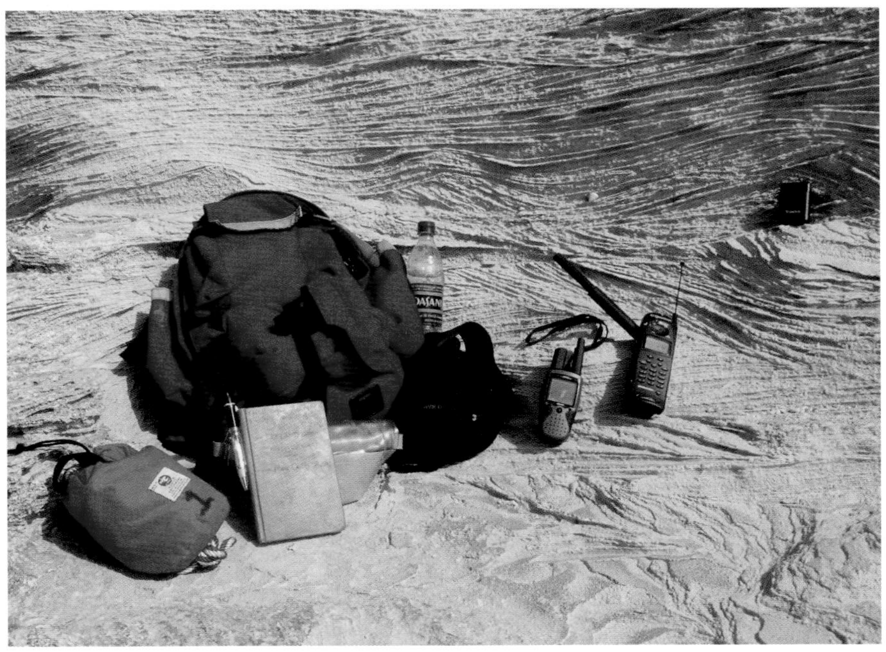

# SECTION 1

## Overview

Although some degree of risk is inherent in every human activity, a primary goal of all field activities should be the safety and health of participants and staff. Those who sponsor, organize, and participate in these field activities have a responsibility to promote and support safety while achieving their technical, educational, or business objectives.

No one goes into the field with the intention of getting injured or killed. Most accidents, at root, result from a loss of perspective, a narrowing of focus, or developing tunnel vision: "I only wanted to get a better look at the rocks by climbing up the cliff/leaning out of the boat/leaving the trail." "Yes, people get hurt doing _____, but it's not going to happen to me." It's like driving down the road only looking ahead but never left, right, or behind—most of the time we get away with it, but such tunnel vision leaves us vulnerable to accidents. And, unfortunately, when an accident happens, it happens with such suddenness and severity that it breaks a person's life in two forever, into "before" and "after."

Experience and complexity theory indicate that it is commonly not one big dumb mistake that leads to an accident, but a series of apparently inconsequential misunderstandings, compromises, and missteps taken out of context, out of a broader perspective. Our field safety process is designed to break that chain, the downhill slide to misfortune, by addressing root causes directly through procedures designed to develop, communicate, and maintain the wider perspective. It draws on the perspective and experience of not only the group actively conducting field operations, but of similar groups in past activities, and of national and international outdoor-activity and safety groups. The entire approach boils down to "Think before you do it" and "Think while you're doing it"—all the rest is help for building, communicating, and documenting a broad safety-based perspective on why we are in the field.

This field safety process was designed to provide a streamlined and scaleable framework for considering field hazards and devising policies and procedures to prevent and mitigate their impact. It works best as an integral part of an organization-wide comprehensive safety and security program. This manual is not intended as an encyclopedic compilation of safety procedures, but as a guide to a methodology for ensuring that appropriate information is considered in planning and conducting field operations. It draws upon a wide range of expertise from national and international safety, outdoors, and industry organizations (see Table 1). This system has been tested

**Table 1.** Partial List of Authorities used in developing safety procedures.

| | |
|---|---|
| American Alpine Club | The Mountaineers |
| American Red Cross | National Fire Protection Association |
| Boy Scouts of America | National Outdoor Leadership School |
| Emergency Cardiac Care Committee, American Heart Association | National Safety Council |
| Girl Scouts of America | YMCA |
| Victorian Institute of Earth Sciences | British Geological Society |


DOI:10.1306/1119797DEG3223

and refined based on decades of ExxonMobil's experience in fieldwork, schools, and trips in countries around the world. During a typical year, more than 500 ExxonMobil geoscientists visit more than 400 sites worldwide while participating in field activities. We have found that the procedures in this manual help ExxonMobil staff to plan field activities better and more efficiently.

## SCOPE

This Field Activity Safety Manual is designed to cover most activities conducted in the field by individuals, groups from schools, universities, companies, and other organizations. The term "Field Activities" encompasses organization or job-related Field Schools, Field Trips, and Fieldwork undertaken or participated in by individuals in an outdoor environment. The term "Organization" refers to the entity to which an individual belongs that has a role in conducting or sponsoring the activity or approving the individual's participation, such as a business, professional society, or university.

This process explicitly excludes trips and excursions to "controlled work environments" such as geophysical surveys, ships, industrial plants, drilling rigs, etc., for which safety plans already exist.

Individuals and groups applying these processes to their activities retain final responsibility for awareness of and compliance with all applicable local laws, regulations, and organizational policies. These considerations are especially important when operating outside the home country of the organization. Potential issues include: accessibility for disabled persons, privacy of personal data, provision of medical services, and regulations concerning communications, safety, and first-aid equipment.

## INTRODUCTION

This Field Activity Safety Manual was developed with the objective of enhancing the safe execution of all Field Activities by standardizing the manner in which the activities are planned and conducted. All forms referred to in this publication are printed in the sections in which they are referred to as well as being on the CD-Rom attached to the inside back cover of this book.

The following overview describes the process for developing a new Field Activity or for planning a new session of a recurring Field Activity. Detailed descriptions of the prescribed tasks and actions are located in the sections that follow the overview. The detailed descriptions also contain references to related procedures and forms that are included as attachments.

This manual was developed by a team with members from ExxonMobil Upstream Research Company, ExxonMobil Exploration Company, and ExxonMobil Upstream SHE group (Safety, Health, and Environment) with a broad range of skills and experience in field operations, emergency response, and safety and risk management with ExxonMobil and other organizations such as the American Red Cross, Boy Scouts, Mountain Rescue Association, and National Safety Council. The process was developed using standard company safety documents and procedures as a basis.

A concerted effort was made to make the process applicable to a broad range of activities and locations. Our recommendations follow currently accepted safety and outdoor work practices. We regret any errors or omissions and encourage the reader to bring these to the authors' attention. We welcome any suggestions for improvement, which can be sent to the authors or to your organization's Geoscience Field Safety Coordinator.

## DEFINITIONS

The following terms and abbreviations will be used throughout this publication:

### Field Activity (Activity)

This term encompasses the following activities undertaken in an outdoors environment, conducted or sponsored by an organization primarily for members of the organization:

- **Field Schools**—training sessions involving visits to sites not covered by other Safety, Health, and Environment (SHE) plans. These are typically recurring events that visit the same locations repeatedly to conduct a set series of learning exercises. Within a company, Field Schools may be coordinated by a Training group.
- **Field Trips**—visits to sites not covered by existing SHE procedures for observation or training or both. These activities are typically non-recurring events and may include many participants, some from outside the sponsoring organization.
- **Fieldwork**—visits to sites not covered by existing SHE procedures for purposes of performing work activities, collecting samples, or both. These activities typically involve small teams of experienced workers on an ad-hoc basis.

**Field School**

**Field Trip**

**Fieldwork**

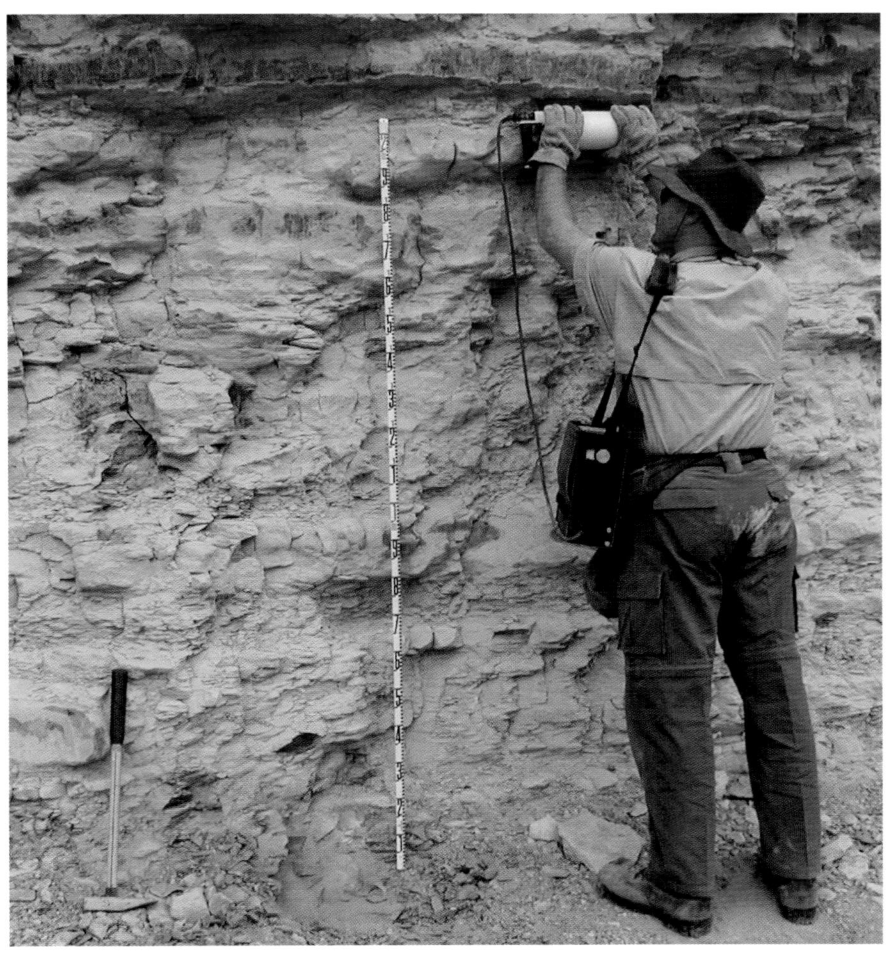

### Field Activities Operated by Others (OBO)

This term includes trips or schools that are not organized or led by a person's home organization. (Any activity that is led by a member of an organization that has adopted this safety process is to be treated as a Field Trip—see above). Since the home organization has no direct control over the preparation and organization of these activities, the individual participants are charged with the majority of their own safety preparations. Section 3 details the participant's responsibilities for these Activities.

## PERSONNEL

Prior to implementing the development process for a specific Activity, an Activity Owner and an Activity Coordinator must be identified. Personnel as well as others involved in planning, conducting, and participating in a Field Activity include:

- **Activity Owner** is the person with direct responsibility for oversight of the described Activity. This is typically a first-line manager in industrial organizations.
- **Activity Coordinator (AC)** is the designated leader of the group actually entering the field to perform the indicated Field Activity.
- **Geoscience Field Safety Coordinator (GFSC)**—A permanent position whose responsibility is to help ensure that the safety and health considerations of all Field Activities have been appropriately and consistently addressed. This person serves as a single point of contact for initiating and conducting this field safety process. She or he also receives feedback on field operations and shares lessons learned with leaders of and participants in future activities.
- **Instructors**—Persons involved in teaching or delivering the message of the Activity.
- **Logistics Coordinator (LC)**—Person responsible for arranging the logistics for the Activity, including lodging, food, transportation, etc.
- **Activity Staff (Staff)**—a generic term for all personnel designated to assist with the preparation and delivery of the Activity—including the AC, Instructors, and LC.

> NOTE: For Fieldwork, all participants are considered to be Activity Staff for the purposes of training and Activity execution.

- **Safety Watch**—The Staff Member charged with safety oversight and first aid response for the Activity on a daily basis. (See an expanded definition in Section 3)
- **Participant**—An organization member or other individual who is taking part in the Activity.

## OVERVIEW OF FIELD ACTIVITY PROCESS

The process provides a systematic, thorough approach to:

- evaluating hazards that may be encountered,
- assembling means and equipment for preventing and mitigating their impact,
- communicating risks and preparations to participants,
- conducting safe field operations, and
- capturing lessons learned and suggestions for future activities.

Following is an overview of the entire process for planning, preparing, and conducting a defined Field Activity (Figure 1). Included are the prescribed dates

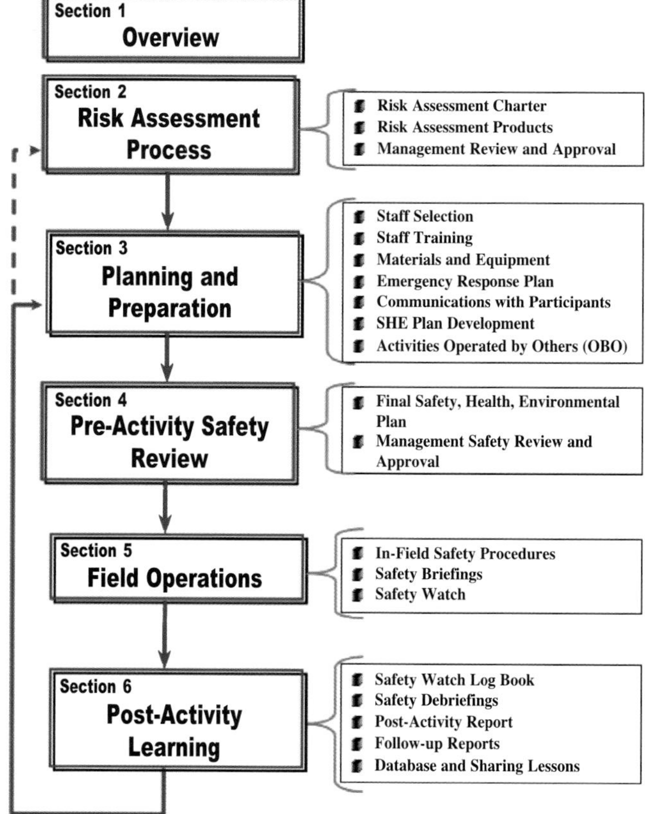


**Figure 1**

(relative to the start of the Activity) by which each step should be completed. Following this overview are sections containing detailed descriptions of the planning and preparation process with forms, examples, etc.

### Develop/Review Field Activity Risk Assessment

A Base Risk Assessment must be in place for each Field Activity no less than 8 weeks before its start. The Base Risk Assessment identifies risks associated with the specific Field Activity, summarizes their consequences and probability of occurrence, and specifies prevention and mitigation measures to be implemented. The Risk Assessment process for each type of Activity is the same, but there are slight differences in the details of the methodology. The ***Risk Assessment Process Description and Charter Procedure*** in Section 2 defines the overall process and specific application in detail. OBO Activities need to be evaluated on a case-by-case basis in consultation with the organizer (see Section 3).

### Prepare for Field Activity

The key to the safe and successful completion of any Field Activity is in the planning and preparation. In roughly chronological order, the general steps are: Coordinator selects staff; Coordinator makes sure that SHE training needed by the Staff is current; Staff reviews the Base Risk Assessment; Staff sends safety and logistical information to participants; Staff receives and reviews medical and disability information from participants; and the Staff modifies plans for SHE, Emergency Response, and course delivery as needed (Section 3). Preparations for an Activity need to be completed during the period from 8 to 2 weeks before the beginning of the Activity.

### Examine Preparations with Independent Reviewer

In a commercial organization, Management approval to conduct an Activity is obtained at a Pre-Activity Safety Review meeting that occurs 1 to 2 weeks before the start of the Activity. In an academic setting, this review can be conducted with an academic supervisor or an experienced peer. The key point is to have a fresh, impartial look at the field plans and preparations by someone who is knowledgeable, experienced, and not directly involved with the particular Field Activity. A discussion and review of the SHE Plan is the centerpiece of this meeting to ensure that all preparations are complete (Section 4).

### Conduct Field Activity Safely

Preparations are put into practice using a set of standard operating procedures and equipment. These include initial, daily, and site-specific safety briefings, protocols for driving, hiking, boating, and swimming, and SHE and Emergency Response plans. The attached ***Field Activity Safety Procedures*** document defines in detail safety-related processes and requirements for Field Activities (Section 5).

### Capture and Share Lessons

An important tool for the continued safe and effective execution of all Field Activities is the identification, capture, and sharing of lessons learned, including proactive reporting of near misses. A one-page ***Field Activity Follow-up*** report provides a framework for this (Section 6).

## QUICK GUIDE CHECKLISTS FOR SAFETY PREPARATIONS

Each of the Activities governed by this manual requires a different level of preparation and documentation as shown below. This is not to imply that the level of SHE preparedness is different, but certain activities allow the use of pre-existing base or generic Risk Assessments, Emergency Response Plans, etc., thereby reducing the amount of pre-Activity effort.

**OBO Field Trips (typically takes 1 hour):**
- ☐ Complete Potential Hazard Register
- ☐ Complete Personal Safety Plan
- ☐ Fill out personal Emergency Medical Information card
- ☐ Discuss preparations with supervisor and obtain endorsement on Personal Safety Plan.

**Fieldwork (small groups, experienced workers)** ***(typically takes 1–2 hours)*****:**

- ☐ Review existing Generic Fieldwork Risk Assessment using Hazard Register (modified as necessary).
- ☐ Complete Emergency Information and Medical Certification form, submit to activity coordinator.
- ☐ Develop a Field Activity SHE Plan (Section 3.6 of this publication), including Emergency Response Plan (use checklist on front page of SHE Plan, includes review of SHE training status).
- ☐ Conduct a Pre-Activity Safety Review Meeting with Activity Owner and obtain endorsement.
- ☐ IF applicable:
  - ☐ *Review host organization SHE Plan and develop bridging document or develop original SHE Plan*
  - ☐ *Non Scheduled/Charter transportation approval (process varies by organization)*
  - ☐ *Foreign Travel approval (process varies by organization)*

**Field Schools (recurrent events, moderate-sized groups, less experienced)** ***(typically takes 2–3 hours once Base Risk Assessment is constructed)*****:**

- ☐ Review existing Risk Assessment and Site-Specific Summary sheets, upgrade as necessary.
- ☐ Select Staff, review their SHE training status *(CPR, First Aid, Defensive Driving, Field Safety Leadership)*
- ☐ Prepare and send out pre-school information package to participants
- ☐ Review and Address Participants' Special Needs.
- ☐ Develop a Field Activity SHE Plan, including Emergency Response Plan (use checklist on front page of SHE Plan). Recommend doing as a staff team approximately 4 weeks before class.
- ☐ Obtain field safety gear (from Field Safety Coordinator or other source)
- ☐ Conduct a Pre-Activity Safety Review Meeting with Activity Owner and obtain endorsement.
- ☐ IF applicable:
  - ☐ *Non-scheduled/Charter transportation approval (process varies by organization)*
  - ☐ *Foreign Travel approval (process varies by organization)*

**Field Trips (one-time events, large groups [>30 participants], wide range of experience)** ***(typically takes 8–16 work hours)*****:**

- ☐ Conduct Risk Assessment using standard process in Risk Assessment Charter, using Standard Hazard Registers.
- ☐ Construct Site Specific Summary sheets for each field site.
- ☐ Select Staff, review their SHE training status *(CPR/First Aid, Defensive Driving, Field Safety Leadership).*
- ☐ Prepare and send out pre-trip information package to participants (by trip coordinator).
- ☐ Review and Address Participants' Special Needs.
- ☐ Develop a Field Activity SHE Plan, including Emergency Response Plan. Recommend doing as a team approximately 4 weeks before class.
- ☐ Obtain field safety gear (from Field Safety Coordinator or other source).
- ☐ Conduct a Pre-Activity Safety Review Meeting with Activity Owner and obtain endorsement.
- ☐ IF applicable:
  - ☐ *Review host organization SHE Plan and develop bridging document or develop original SHE Plan*
  - ☐ *Non-scheduled/Charter transportation approval (process varies by organization)*
  - ☐ *Foreign Travel approval (process varies by organization)*

**For all Field Activities:**

- ☐ Complete Field Activity Follow-up Report within 2 weeks of return and forward to Geoscience Field Safety Coordinator.

**Table 2.** Overview of Field Activity Safety Preparations.

| | OBO | Work | School | Trip |
|---|---|---|---|---|
| **Risk Assessment:** | | | | |
| » Construct NEW Risk Assessment | | | | X |
| » REVIEW existing Risk Assessment | | X | X | |
| – Use Standard Hazard Register | X | X | X | X |
| – Use Participant Information Forms | | X | X | X |
| **SHE Plan:** | | | | |
| » Personal Safety Plan | X | | | |
| » SHE Plan | | X | X | X |
| – Site Safety Summary Sheet | | | X | X |
| » Emergency Response Plan (ERP) | | X | X | X |
| – Bridge to Host Organization Plan | | (X) | | (X) |
| **Participant Emergency and Medical Information:** | | | | |
| » Personal Medical Information Form | X | | | |
| » Emergency Information and Medical Certification | | X | X | X |
| **Travel Clearances:** | | | | |
| » Non-scheduled/Charter Transportation Approval | (X) | (X) | (X) | (X) |
| » Foreign Travel Approval | (X) | (X) | (X) | (X) |
| **Safety Gear:** | | | | |
| » PPE as required | X | X | X | X |
| » Safety Watch Backpack | | (X) | X | X |
| **Safety Observations:** | | | | |
| » Safety Log Book | | | X | X |
| » Field Activity Follow-up Report | X | X | X | X |

*X = Required; (X) = As Necessary.*

# 2 Risk Assessment

Overview

**Risk Assessment Process**

Planning and Preparation

Pre-Activity Safety Review

Field Operations

Pre-Activity Learning

*"Be prepared to do that thing the moment the accident does occur. But the great thing for you Scouts to bear in mind is that wherever you are, and whatever you are doing, you should think to yourself, 'What accident is likely to occur here?' and, 'What is my duty if it occurs?'"*

*Baden-Powell, 1908*

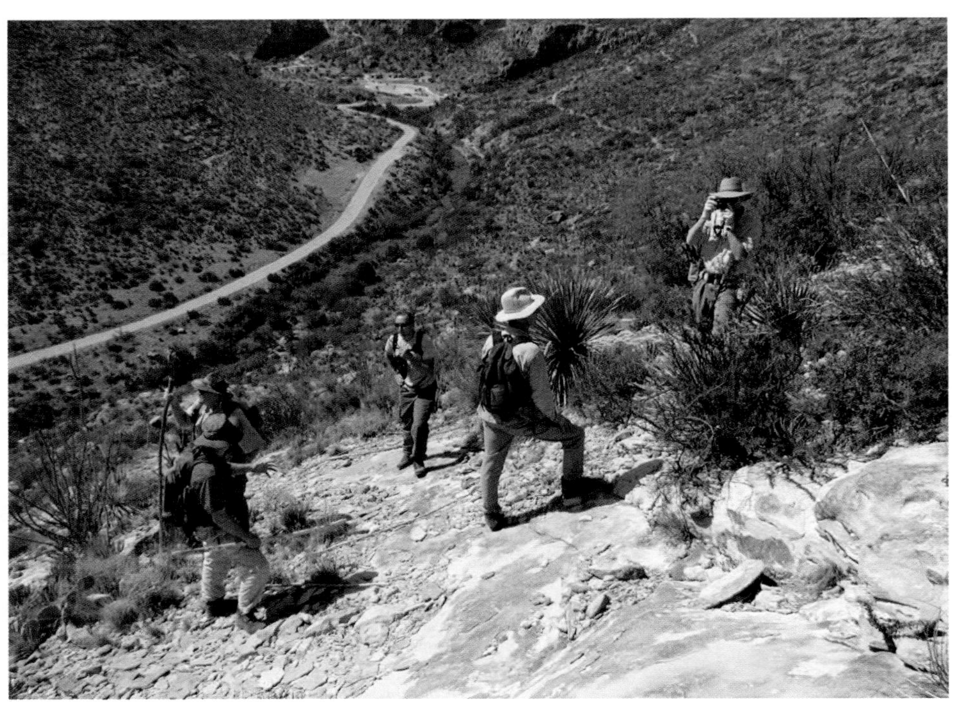

# SECTION 2

## Risk Assessment Process

A Base Risk Assessment must be in place for each Field Activity. The Risk Assessment process for each type of Activity is the same, but there are slight differences in the detailed methodology. The detailed process for conducting the Risk Assessment is specified in a Risk Assessment Charter, written by the Activity Owner and Activity Coordinator based on the sample charter included in this section. The Charter identifies the people who are to conduct the Risk Assessment and specifies the scope of their activities, products, and time lines. The example ***Risk Assessment Process Description and Charter*** (on the following pages) defines the overall process and specific application in detail.

### FIELD SCHOOLS

A **Base Risk Assessment** is to be conducted every **3 or 5 years** for each specific school, depending on the level of the assessed risk (every 3 years for intermediate or higher risk—every 5 years for lower risk activities.)

A session-specific Risk Assessment review is to be conducted **2–3 months** prior to the scheduled start date, incorporating any new information or field conditions, and lessons learned from previous sessions and other field activities.

### FIELD TRIPS

By definition these are usually one-time events. Therefore a **trip-specific Risk Assessment** must be conducted for each Trip. It should be completed **1–2 months** prior to the Trip. Check with the Field Safety Coordinator to see whether a Risk Assessment exists for a previous Trip to the same or a similar location.

### FIELDWORK

A **Generic Fieldwork Risk Assessment** covering all Fieldwork will be conducted every 5 years (the assessed level being "Lower Risk"). The Geoscience Field Safety Coordinator will lead this Risk Assessment Team, composed of experienced fieldworkers.

Specific Fieldwork projects are to be evaluated relative to the Base Risk Assessment no later than **1–2 weeks** prior to the scheduled start.

**The following forms for this section are also located on the CD-Rom accompanying this book:**

Field Activity Risk Assessment Summary Report: Blank—2A

Field Activity Risk Assessment: Potential Hazards Register—2B

Field Activity Risk Assessment Checklist—2C

Risk Assessment Summary Report: Generic Fieldwork—2D

*(text continues on page 35)*


DOI:10.1306/1119798DEG3223

## Activity Risk Matrix

2A

Activity/School:

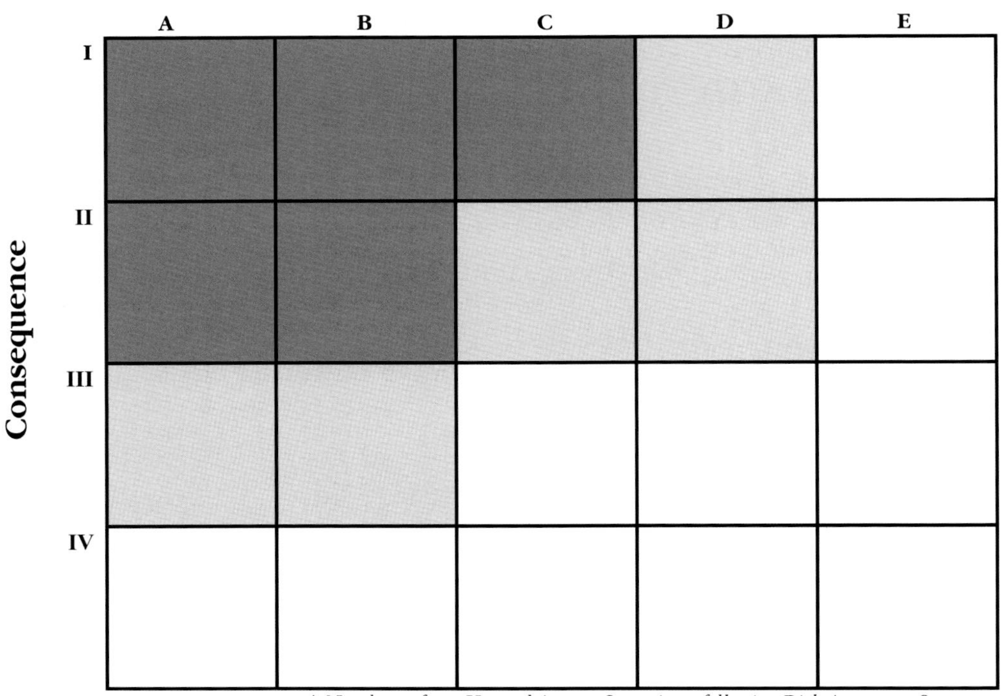


** Numbers refer to Hazard Area or Scenario on following Risk Assessment Summary*

| CONSEQUENCE CATEGORY | CONSIDERATIONS | | | |
|---|---|---|---|---|
| | HEALTH/SAFETY | PUBLIC DISRUPTION | ENVIRONMENTAL IMPACT | FINANCIAL IMPACT |
| I | FATALITIES/SERIOUS IMPACT ON PUBLIC | LARGE COMMUNITY | MAJOR/EXTENDED DURATION/ FULL SCALE RESPONSE | CORPORATE/ Organization Wide |
| II | SERIOUS INJURY TO PERSONNEL/ LIMITED IMPACT ON PUBLIC | SMALL COMMUNITY | SERIOUS/SIGNIFICANT RESOURCE COMMITMENT | REGION/ Single Country |
| III | MEDICAL TREATMENT FOR PERSONNEL/NO IMPACT ON PUBLIC | MINOR | MODERATE/LIMITED RESPONSE OF SHORT DURATION | DIVISION/ Single Site |
| IV | MINOR IMPACT ON PERSONNEL | MINIMAL TO NONE | MINOR/LITTLE OR NO RESPONSE NEEDED | GROUP/ Individual Unit |

| PROBABILITY CATEGORY | DEFINITION |
|---|---|
| A | POSSIBILITY OF REPEATED INCIDENTS (>10 per 50 sessions (=1 yr)) |
| B | POSSIBILITY OF ISOLATED INCIDENTS (2–10 per 50 sessions (=1 yr)) |
| C | POSSIBILITY OF OCCURRING SOMETIME (1 per 50 sessions (=1 yr)) |
| D | NOT LIKELY TO OCCUR (1 per 500 sessions (=10 yr)) |
| E | PRACTICALLY IMPOSSIBLE (<1 per 5000 sessions (=100 yr)) |

Field Activity Safety Process 2B

## Field Activity Risk Assessment - Potential Hazards Register

Field Activity: ______________________ Dates: ______________
Site Name: ______________________

| Potential Hazard | Probability of Occurrence | | | | Comments<br>Issues-Mitigators-Scenarios |
|---|---|---|---|---|---|
| | H | M | L | NA | |
| **Natural Environment** | | | | | |
| Temperature Extremes (Hot/Cold) | | | | | |
| Uneven/Slippery Walking Surfaces | | | | | |
| Sharp Objects—rocks, coral, vegetation | | | | | |
| Heights/Drop-offs (including high elevation) | | | | | |
| Falling Objects/Obstructions | | | | | |
| Tight Spaces/Narrow Openings/Overhangs | | | | | |
| Darkness/Low Light | | | | | |
| Strong Sunlight (including sunburn) | | | | | |
| Foul Weather—wind, rain, snow, lightning, flash flood | | | | | |
| Fire Hazard | | | | | |
| Smoke/Dust/Fog | | | | | |
| Toxic/Allergic Sources (vegetation, pollen) | | | | | |
| Animals—insects, reptiles, mammals, other | | | | | |
| Water/Current—streams, waves, tides, depth | | | | | |
| **Man-Made Environment (for Pedestrians)** | | | | | |
| Vehicular Traffic—roads, railroads | | | | | |
| Bridges | | | | | |
| Fences | | | | | |
| Utility Lines | | | | | |
| Local Inhabitants (including hunters) | | | | | |
| Crowds/Spectators | | | | | |
| **Transportation (Auto, Boat, Air)** | | | | | |
| Vehicle Condition *(safety equipment, mechanical, tires, etc.)* | | | | | |
| Driver Qualification/Experience for location | | | | | |
| Route Conditions—rough (inc. flat tires) | | | | | |
| Route Conditions—congestion | | | | | |
| Route Conditions—winding, limited sight line | | | | | |
| Pedestrians | | | | | |
| Intersections/Railroad Crossings | | | | | |
| **Human Factors/Participant Activities** | | | | | |
| Hiking/Walking | | | | | |
| Climbing | | | | | |
| Lifting/Carrying | | | | | |
| Swimming/Snorkeling/SCUBA/Boating | | | | | |
| Digging/Trenching | | | | | |
| Use of Tools (including chipping) | | | | | |
| Extended Immobility (auto, boat, air) | | | | | |
| Fatigue/Dehydration | | | | | |
| Food Handling | | | | | |
| Language/Culture Differences | | | | | |
| Pre-Existing Physical/Medical Needs | | | | | |
| Separation of Individuals from Group | | | | | |
| Lack of Rest Stops/Facilities | | | | | |
| Individual Behaviors/Risk Acceptance | | | | | |
| Equipment Failure | | | | | |
| **Other Factors** | | | | | |
| Limited/Remote Medical Services | | | | | |
| Limited Communications | | | | | |
| *Additional Hazards identified by team?* | | | | | |

Field Activity Safety Process **2B**

## Field Activity Risk Assessment - Potential Hazards Register

*Include notes on local conditions:*

*What is the probability of: 1. an occurrence with serious consequences (levels I, II, or III), or 2. many/frequent incidents with level IV consequences during a single session or site visit?*

*Notes on local issues, important safeguards to use, and scenarios to be assessed*

| Potential Hazard | Probability of Occurrence H | M | L | NA | Comments Issues-Mitigators-Scenarios |
|---|---|---|---|---|---|
| **Natural Environment** — *Criteria, Limits, Critical Factors to consider:* | | | | | |
| Temperature Extremes (Hot/Cold) ≅ *Temperature (>30°C, <5°C), Wind, Humidity* | | | | | *Length of Exposure, Time of Year/Day* |
| Uneven/Slippery Walking Surfaces ≅ *Slip, trip, or fall that results in injury* | | | | | *Cumulative Fatigue, Weather* |
| Sharp Objects—rocks, coral, vegetation ≅ *Contact or fall results in penetrating wound/scratched cornea* | | | | | *Visibility, Fatigue, Exact Route* |
| Heights/Drop-offs (inc. high elevation) ≅ *Fall that results in free-fall drop of more than 2 m* | | | | | *Slope/softness of "landing" zone* |
| Falling Objects/Obstructions ≅ *Spontaneous/Participant-caused, capable of causing serious injury* | | | | | *Time of year, freshness of outcrop* |
| Tight Spaces/Narrow Openings/Overhangs ≅ *Results in impact or crushing injury, or panic/distress* | | | | | *Visibility, crowding,* |
| Darkness/Low Light ≅ *Contributing factor to other hazards that result in injury* | | | | | *Visibility, Fatigue, Weather* |
| Strong Sunlight (inc. sunburn) ≅ *Serious sunburn, "snow" blindness, contributing factor to fatigue* | | | | | *Exposure length, surface albedo* |
| Foul Weather Considerations—wind, rain, snow, lightning, flash flood ≅ *Local, upstream* | | | | | *Before & During activity* |
| Fire Hazard ≅ *Hot vehicle exhaust system/discarded cigarette causes fire, traps group, endangers ecosystem* | | | | | *Access to site during fire bans* |
| Smoke/Dust/Fog ≅ *Causes eye/throat/nose injury, contributing factor to other hazards* | | | | | *Time of year/day* |
| Toxic/Allergic Sources (vegetation, pollen) ≅ *Causes acute reaction, contributing factor to other hazards* | | | | | *Time of year, EMS access* |
| Animals—insects, reptiles, mammals, other ≅ *Causes trauma, envenomation, allergic reaction* | | | | | *Time of year, local experience* |
| Water/Current ≅ *Fall results in submersion, Strenuous exertion in water triggers pre-existing medical condition* | | | | | *Time of day/year, Hypothermia* |
| **Man-Made Environment (for Pedestrians)** | | | | | |
| Vehicular Traffic—roads, railroads ≅ *Vehicle impacts participant, Group activity causes traffic hazard* | | | | | *Time of day/year* |
| Bridges ≅ *Vehicle impacts participant, Group activity causes traffic hazard* | | | | | *Sidewalk, width of shoulder* |
| Fences ≅ *If gate not available, crossing results in fall, impact, lacerations, penetrating wound* | | | | | *Property owner interactions* |
| Utility Lines ≅ *Approach route or portions of outcrop allow contact with power lines, resulting in injury* | | | | | *Alternate routes* |
| Local Inhabitants (inc. hunters) ≅ *Group provokes hazardous reaction from locals; distraction factor* | | | | | *Time of year/day* |
| Crowds/Spectators ≅ *Group provokes hazardous reaction from locals; distraction factor* | | | | | *Time of year/day* |
| **Transportation (Auto, Boat, Air)** | | | | | |
| Vehicle Condition ≅ *Primary or contributing factor to accident/collision* | | | | | *Rental company, local experience* |
| Driver Qualification/Experience for location ≅ *Primary or contributing factor to accident/collision* | | | | | *Availability of local drivers* |
| Route Conditions—rough (inc. flat tires) ≅ *Rough enough to be contributing factor to accident/collision* | | | | | *Type of vehicle used, local drivers* |
| Route Conditions—congestion ≅ *Enough to be contributing factor to accident, esp. around airport and major cities* | | | | | *Time of day, Route selection* |
| Route Conditions—winding, limited sight line ≅ *Enough to be contributing factor to accident/collision* | | | | | *Time of day, Route selection* |
| Pedestrians ≅ *Sufficiently numerous or common to be contributing factor to accident* | | | | | *Time of day, Route selection* |
| Intersections/Railroad Crossings ≅ *Hazardous/Unguarded/Confusing location contributes to accident* | | | | | *Time of day, Route selection* |
| **Human Factors/Participant Activities** | | | | | |
| Hiking/Walking ≅ *Intensity, length, duration, cumulative exertion sufficient to trigger illness, contribute to injury* | | | | | *Time of day/year, Weather* |
| Climbing ≅ *Requires use of both hands to ascend/descend more than 2 m vertical, exposure to fall & injury* | | | | | *Weather, outcrop condition* |
| Lifting/Carrying ≅ *Improper technique/overloaded backpacks results in injury* | | | | | *Gear selection, individual fitness* |
| Swimming/Snorkeling/SCUBA/Boating ≅ *Improper technique/conditioning/equipment causes injury* | | | | | *Pre-trip screening, PFD policy* |
| Digging/Trenching ≅ *Digging causes injury to self or other participant, Trench collapse causes injury* | | | | | *OSHA rules for deep trenches* |
| Use of Tools (inc. chipping) ≅ *Improper technique/equipment causes injury to self or other participant* | | | | | *Required PPE* |
| Extended Immobility ≅ *Enough to be contributing factor to accident, trigger pre-existing medical condition* | | | | | *Agenda/Travel planning* |
| Fatigue/Dehydration ≅ *Enough to be contributing factor to accident, trigger pre-existing medical condition* | | | | | *Agenda, Time of year/day* |
| Food Handling ≅ *Improper technique/equipment contributes to food-borne illness* | | | | | *Training, Sanitation facilities* |
| Language/Culture Differences ≅ *Contributing factor to accident* | | | | | *Pre-trip participant information* |
| Pre-Existing Physical/Medical Needs ≅ *Contributing factor to accident, acute episode of illness* | | | | | *Pre-trip participant information* |
| Separation of Individuals from Group ≅ *Contributing factor to accident* | | | | | *Safety briefings, Read backs* |
| Lack of Rest Stops/Facilities ≅ *Contributing factor to fatigue, accident* | | | | | *Pre-trip planning* |
| Individual Behaviors/Risk Acceptance ≅ *Contributing factor to accident* | | | | | *Management letter, briefings* |
| Equipment Failure ≅ *Sufficiently critical and serious to be contributing factor to accident* | | | | | *Pre-trip planning, inspections* |
| **Other Factors** | | | | | |
| Limited/Remote Medical Services ≅ *Consequence of injury/illness escalates due to remoteness* | | | | | *Pre-trip plan, communications* |
| Limited Communications ≅ *Consequence of injury/illness escalates due to delayed access to EMS assistance* | | | | | *Pre-trip planning, field checks* |
| *Additional Hazards identified by team?* ≅ *Significantly different, likely to have serious consequences* | | | | | *Consult local experts, experience* |

## Field Activity Safety Process 2C

# Preparation Checklist for Risk Assessment of Field Activity

This checklist is provided to assist in compiling the information and materials required to conduct or review a Risk Assessment prior to a Field Activity.

### Required Information and Resources

- ❑ Maps and photos of the stops or areas to be assessed
- ❑ Guidebooks, publications, etc.
- ❑ Activities to be assessed—when (time of year, time of day); how they will be conducted.
- ❑ Activity definition—physical requirements of the participants (suitable for a pre-Activity letter)
- ❑ Activity agenda (with safety orientations built in for schools and trips)
- ❑ Environmental conditions—weather, tide tables, etc.
- ❑ Travel Advisories— *see organization and government sources (e.g. travel.state.gov)*
- ❑ Contractor/local organization safety documents (example—charter boat company, ERP)
- ❑ Out of bounds areas associated with the activity—cliff edge, rapids, reef boundaries, etc.
- ❑ Access to medical, rescue, and EMS services—distance, time, contacts.
- ❑ List of PPE, required equipment, and tools—boots, hard hats, mobile phones, picks, shovels, etc.
- ❑ Communications capabilities (Cell phones, satellite phones, radios)
- ❑ Incident and near miss data from previous similar trips.

### Recommended additional information

- ❑ Participants' training and background information—experience, SHE training, background, home group/company.
- ❑ Local emergency response information—law enforcement, fire department.
- ❑ Go/No Go criteria—for travel to and from activity and each site and field activity.

**NOTE: Provide any additional information and materials that will enable the risk assessment team to accurately evaluate the Activity.**

# RISK ASSESSMENT SUMMARY REPORT:
## Fieldwork (Generic)



- **Activity/Situation**
  Briefly describe the activity or situation that involves a health, safety, or environmental risk to personnel and/or property.
  - **Driving—Equipment failure:** Accident occurs at high speed on a highway (single vehicle rollover or multi-vehicle accident).
  - **Driving—Limited site lines:** Accident occurs on winding mountain road, busy interstate, or in low-visibility conditions (weather or low light).
  - **Vehicular traffic—Pedestrian:** Participant is struck by a vehicle while working along a road or railroad.
  - **Boating—Equipment failure:** Water vehicle sinks due to breached hull, collision with submerged object, or broken rudder or prop causing swamping/capsizing and participant becomes injured or drowns.
  - **Heights/Drop-off:** Participant disregards all instructions, goes too close to cliff edge and falls over, dropping more than 10 m.
  - **Waves/Current:** Participant working near water, loses footing or is swept into the water by a wave.
  - **Swimming, wading, snorkeling:** Participant takes in water through snorkel or cannot catch breath while swimming and submerges.
  - **Fatigue/Dehydration:** Participant becomes fatigued or dehydrated while driving, snorkeling, or hiking and looses consciousness.
  - **Language or culture differences:** Participant does not understand instructions or safety orientation and enters an area that is designated out of bounds and becomes injured.
  - **Pre-existing Physical or Medical needs:** Participant does not identify or disregards pre-existing condition while participating in an activity designated as strenuous.
  - **Separation from group and individual risk acceptance:** Participant disregards safety orientation or instructions and enters an area designated as out of bounds and becomes injured.

- **Potential Consequences/Probabilities**
  Describe the nature of the risk and the possible health, safety, or environmental consequences if it is not properly managed.
  1. **Fatality—Vehicular accident/E**
  2. **Fatality—Vehicular accident/E**
  3. **Fatality—Run over by vehicle/E**
  4. **Fatality—Drowning/E**
  5. **Fatality—Fall from cliff/E**
  6. **Fatality—Drowning/E**
  7. **Fatality—Drowning/E**
  8. **Fatality—Vehicular accident and/or Drowning—Fall from cliff/E**
  9. **Fatality—Drowning and/or Fall from cliff/E**
  10. **Fatality—Drowning and/or Fall from cliff/E**
  11. **Fatality—Drowning and/or Fall from cliff/E**

- **Procedures/Actions to Manage Risk**
  Describe the procedures/actions, if any, being used to manage the risk. Consider preventative measures such as safety procedures, inspections, equipment standards, alarm/trip devices and training, as well as mitigation measures such as response procedures/training and protective gear/equipment/devices.

  1. Driver screening and qualification, Driver familiarity with equipment, Use of navigator, Driving protocols, Safety orientation
  2. Driver screening and qualification, Emergency Response Plan (ERP), Driver familiarity, Safety briefings, Safety debriefings
  3. Safety watch, Safety vests, Safety briefings, Vehicle placement, Traffic control devices, Crossing guards
  4. Charter company certification, Boat operators' qualifications and familiarity with route, Watercraft inspection, Wearing of Personal Flotation Device (PFD/Life Jacket) of appropriate type and rating at all times on board watercraft, Emergency Response Plan

## Field Activity Safety Process 2D

5. Safety orientation, Participants stay more than 10 ft (3 m) from all dropoffs ("10-foot rule"), Hiking protocol, Out of bounds clearly defined
6. Go/No-Go criteria, Safety briefing, Emergency Response Plan
7. Go/No-Go criteria, Buddy watch, Safety briefing, Emergency Response Plan
8. Driver screening/qualification, Driver familiarity, Safety briefings, multiple qualified drivers, Go/No-Go criteria, Buddy watch, Emergency Response Plan, Safety orientation, 10-foot rule, Hiking protocol, Out of bounds clearly defined
9. Go/No-Go criteria, Buddy watch, Emergency Response Plan, Safety orientation, 10-foot rule, Hiking protocol, Out of bounds clearly defined
10. Go/No-Go criteria, Buddy watch, Emergency Response Plan, Safety orientation, 10-foot rule, Hiking protocol, Out of bounds clearly defined
11. Go/No-Go criteria, Buddy watch, Emergency Response Plan, Safety orientation, 10-foot rule, Hiking protocol, Out of bounds clearly defined

- **Risk Level Matrix**

| | A | B | C | D | E |
|---|---|---|---|---|---|
| I | | | | | 1,2,3,4, 5,6,7, 8,9,10, 11 |
| II | | | | | X |
| III | | | X | X | X |
| IV | | | X | X | |

**Assessed Risk Level: LOWER**

- **Date and Authors of Most Recent Risk Evaluation:** ____________ **RA Team:** ____________

- **Approved Plans:**
I hereby approve the plans and/or procedures, responsibilities, and time frames for additional steps that will be implemented to better manage the risk.

**Activity Owner:** ____________ **Date Approved:** ____________

## Activity Detailed Risk Summary

2D

### Activity/School: **Generic Fieldwork on Outcrops**

**Probability**

| Consequence | A | B | C | D | E |
|---|---|---|---|---|---|
| I | | | | | 1,2,12,18,19,32, 34,35,36,37,38* |
| II | | | | | 3,5,7,8,11,13,17, 20,25,30,31,39, 40 |
| III | | | 4,10,28 | 9,15,16,21,23,24, 28 | 14,22,33 |
| IV | | | 29 | 6,26,27,41 | |

** Numbers refer to Hazard Area or Scenario on following Risk Assessment Summary*

| CONSEQUENCE CATEGORY | CONSIDERATIONS | | | |
|---|---|---|---|---|
| | HEALTH/SAFETY | PUBLIC DISRUPTION | ENVIRONMENTAL IMPACT | FINANCIAL IMPACT |
| I | FATALITIES/SERIOUS IMPACT ON PUBLIC | LARGE COMMUNITY | MAJOR/EXTENDED DURATION/ FULL SCALE RESPONSE | CORPORATE/ Organization Wide |
| II | SERIOUS INJURY TO PERSONNEL/ LIMITED IMPACT ON PUBLIC | SMALL COMMUNITY | SERIOUS/SIGNIFICANT RESOURCE COMMITMENT | REGION/ Single Country |
| III | MEDICAL TREATMENT FOR PERSONNEL/NO IMPACT ON PUBLIC | MINOR | MODERATE/LIMITED RESPONSE OF SHORT DURATION | DIVISION/ Single Site |
| IV | MINOR IMPACT ON PERSONNEL | MINIMAL TO NONE | MINOR/LITTLE OR NO RESPONSE NEEDED | GROUP/ Individual Unit |

| PROBABILITY CATEGORY | DEFINITION |
|---|---|
| A | POSSIBILITY OF REPEATED INCIDENTS (>10 per 50 sessions (=1 yr)) |
| B | POSSIBILITY OF ISOLATED INCIDENTS (2–10 per 50 sessions (=1 yr)) |
| C | POSSIBILITY OF OCCURRING SOMETIME (1 per 50 sessions (=1 yr)) |
| D | NOT LIKELY TO OCCUR (1 per 500 sessions (=10 yr)) |
| E | PRACTICALLY IMPOSSIBLE (<1 per 5000 sessions (=100 yr)) |

# Activity Detailed Risk Summary 2D

## Activity/School: Generic Fieldwork on Outcrops

### Risk Assessment Summary

Activity/School: **Generic Fieldwork — Outcrops**

Field Site/Activity: **Use of vehicles (including boats) and driving**

| | Hazard Area | Event/Scenario | Prevention and Mitigation Measures in Place | Con. | Prob. | Extra Measures |
|---|---|---|---|---|---|---|
| 1. | Equipment Failure | Mechanical failure resulting in collision:<br>- Land vehicles (brakes, steering, tire nuts, flat tire)<br>- Boats (rudders, motors, hull) | - Vehicle inspection<br>- Screened rental or charter agency<br>- Defensive Driving<br>- Boat operators' experience<br>- Emergency Response Plan | I | E | None |
| 2. | Limited sight lines | Collision due to fog or winding roads | - Defensive Driving<br>- Go/NoGo criteria<br>- Emergency Response Plan<br>- Alcohol/drug policy<br>- Safety briefings | I | E | None |
| 3. | Foul Weather | Heavy Rain | - Fieldwork scheduling<br>- Weather watch<br>- Go/NoGo criteria<br>- Emergency Response Plan | II | E | None |
| 4. | Foreign Driving | Collision due to inexperience with opposite side driving or foreign country procedures | - Defensive Driving<br>- Use of experienced drivers in foreign countries<br>- Go/NoGo criteria<br>- Emergency Response Plan<br>- Alcohol/drug policy<br>- Safety briefings | III | C | None |
| 5. | Exiting boats to shore — motion/ slick surfaces | Participant slips between boat and shore — sustains cuts or blunt trauma injury | - Boat operators' experience<br>- Emergency Response Plan<br>- First Aid and CPR training<br>- Fieldwork team orientation and assistance | II | E | |
| 6. | All other driving hazards | Minor accidents | - Defensive Driving<br>- Emergency Response Plan<br>- Alcohol/drug policy<br>- Safety briefings | IV | D | None |

## Activity Detailed Risk Summary 2D

## Activity/School: Generic Fieldwork on Outcrops

**Risk Assessment Summary**

Activity/School: **Generic Land-based Fieldwork**

Field Site: **Outcrops**

| | Hazard Area | Event | Prevention and Mitigation Measures in Place | Con. | Prob. | Extra |
|---|---|---|---|---|---|---|
| 7. | Temperature extremes—hot | High temperature and humidity, participant suffers heat stroke (progresses beyond unrecognized heat exhaustion) | - Time of year for fieldwork<br>- Time of day for particular sites (for the shade)<br>- Proper clothing, hat<br>- Safety Briefing<br>- Adequate hydration<br>- First Aid training<br>- Group interaction and ongoing assessment | II | E | None |
| 8. | Temperature extremes—cold | Participant gets wet during course of work during relatively cool weather, progresses into mild hypothermia, and suffers accident due to impaired judgement/coordination | - First Aid training<br>- Safety Briefing<br>- Group interaction and ongoing assessment<br>- PPE<br>- Time of year<br>- Take breaks<br>- Adequate hydration<br>- Extra dry clothing<br>- Proper clothing, hat | II | E | None |
| 9. | Uneven/slippery walking surface | Participants slips, falls, fractures bone (arm, leg) | - First Aid training<br>- Proper footwear<br>- Walking stick<br>- Route selection<br>- Safety Briefing<br>- Group interaction and ongoing assessment<br>- Awareness of physical limitations<br>- Reasonable pacing of physical exertion<br>- Reasonable work schedule to avoid fatigue<br>- Schedule work during daylight hours, remembering time to hike out<br>- Make sure backpacks are properly balanced and not overloaded | III | D | None |

## Activity Detailed Risk Summary 2D

Activity/School: **Generic Fieldwork on Outcrops**

| | Hazard Area | Event | Prevention and Mitigation Measures in Place | Con. | Prob. | Extra |
|---|---|---|---|---|---|---|
| 10. | Sharp objects | Participant accidentally lacerates self on sharp rock, pierced by cactus spine, scratches eye on branch | - Eye protection<br>- Long pants, shirt<br>- Gloves<br>- Proper footwear<br>- Walking stick<br>- Route selection<br>- Safety briefing<br>- Reasonable pacing of physical exertion<br>- Reasonable work schedule to avoid fatigue | III | C | None |
| 11. | Heights/Drop offs <10 m | Participant falls from height between ~2–10 m | - First Aid training<br>- Proper footwear<br>- Walking stick<br>- Route selection<br>- Stay away from edge<br>- Safety Briefing<br>- Group interaction and ongoing assessment<br>- Awareness of physical limitations<br>- Reasonable pacing of physical exertion<br>- Reasonable work schedule to avoid fatigue | II | E | None |
| 12. | Heights/Drop offs >10 m | Participant falls from height >10 m | - First Aid training<br>- Proper footwear<br>- Walking stick<br>- Route selection<br>- Stay away from edge<br>- Safety Briefing<br>- Group interaction and ongoing assessment<br>- Awareness of physical limitations<br>- Reasonable pacing of physical exertion<br>- Reasonable work schedule to avoid fatigue | I | E | None |

## Activity Detailed Risk Summary 2D

### Activity/School: **Generic Fieldwork on Outcrops**

| | Hazard Area | Event | Prevention and Mitigation Measures in Place | Con. | Prob. | Extra |
|---|---|---|---|---|---|---|
| 13. | Falling objects | Participant gets hit on head by falling object dislodged by other member of party | - Safety Briefing<br>- Route selection<br>- Communication among field party<br>- Awareness of stability of outcrop face, esp. when digging for samples<br>- Awareness of others in area not part of field party<br>- Time of year—avoid spring thaw, fall freeze and breakup<br>- Awareness of changing weather (winds, rain, frosts) | II | E | Wear PPE in mine, quarry, or near other very fresh or unstable outcrop faces |
| 14. | Tight spaces/ overhangs | Participant accidentally impacts head on overhang while walking/describing section, sustains laceration or superficial hematoma | - Safety briefing<br>- Awareness of hazards<br>- Selection of areas to be worked<br>- Consider use of PPE if overhangs are common and need to be worked | III | E | None |
| 15. | Foul weather | Weather suddenly changes, participant is scrambling to leave outcrop, slips, falls, and sustains injury | - Time of year<br>- Weather watch, awareness of forecast<br>- Lightning detector<br>- Weather radio<br>- Anti-fall protocols listed above<br>- Selection of sites to be worked under unsettled weather conditions<br>- Go/No Go criteria | III | D | None |
| 16. | Animals—envenomation (North America) *{Foreign field work needs to be assessed separately}* | Participant sustains venomous bite, sting, or localized allergic reactions | - First Aid training<br>- Safety briefing<br>- Pre-trip medical screening for dangerous allergies<br>- Gloves<br>- First Aid kit<br>- Snakebite kit if appropriate<br>- Awareness of animal habitats and habits<br>- Emergency communications equipment<br>- ERP | III | D | None |

## Activity Detailed Risk Summary 2D

### Activity/School: Generic Fieldwork on Outcrops

| | Hazard Area | Event | Prevention and Mitigation Measures in Place | Con. | Prob. | Extra |
|---|---|---|---|---|---|---|
| 17. | Animals—large carnivore | Participant attacked by bear or cougar | - Safety briefing<br>- Awareness of animal habitats and habits<br>- Anti-animal warning devices<br>- Anti-animal defense devices<br>- Contract bear watch as appropriate<br>- Always work in groups<br>- Emergency communications equipment<br>- ERP | II | E | None |
| 18. | Water/Current | Participant working near water, loses footing or swept into water by wave, and drowns | - Timing of visit to intertidal outcrops<br>- Training (ARC "Basic Water Safety and Rescue or equivalent")<br>- Appropriate footwear<br>- Hiking stick<br>- Loosen backpack straps and waistbelt near water<br>- Selection of route/outcrops<br>- Rescue throw bag<br>- Consider use of PFD if most of time spent near water<br>- Awareness of water and shore conditions (waves, tides, level) | I | E | None |
| 19. | Vehicular traffic—pedestrian | Participant hit by vehicle while working along road or railroad | - Safety briefing<br>- Maintain safe distance from traffic<br>- Awareness of local traffic customs, laws, etc (left/right hand driving...)<br>- Traffic vests<br>- Traffic control devices<br>- Safe parking spot<br>- Designate traffic lookout<br>- Time of day and week for working outcrops | I | E | None |

## Activity Detailed Risk Summary 2D

### Activity/School: **Generic Fieldwork on Outcrops**

| | Hazard Area | Event | Prevention and Mitigation Measures in Place | Con. | Prob. | Extra |
|---|---|---|---|---|---|---|
| 20. | Local inhabitants | Participant accidentally shot by hunter | - Avoid hunting season for field work<br>- Wear orange vests/caps<br>- Obtain permits for land access<br>- Safety briefing<br>- Awareness of local customs and inhabitants | II | E | None |
| 21. | Lifting and carrying | Participant injures back while lifting load that is too heavy or improperly lifted | - Safety briefing<br>- Safe lifting techniques<br>- Proper conditioning<br>- Medical screening information<br>- Adequate personnel for the task | III | D | None |
| 22. | Digging/ Trenching | Trench collapses and injures participant (esp. in soft sediments) | - No trenches deeper than waist height<br>- Always have clear escape route<br>- *Check to see if OSHA requirements triggered by activity!* | III | E | None |
| 23. | Use of hand tools | Tool slips and strikes participant or co-worker extremity causing injury | - Training in use of tool<br>- Frequent inspection of tools<br>- Safety glasses<br>- Gloves<br>- Other PPE as needed<br>- Safety briefing<br>- Hand guards on chisels, etc.<br>- Awareness of location of others<br>- Maintain safe area around person using tool<br>- Change out workers to avoid fatigue | III | D | None |

# Activity Detailed Risk Summary 2D

## Activity/School: Generic Fieldwork on Outcrops

| | Hazard Area | Event | Prevention and Mitigation Measures in Place | Con. | Prob. | Extra |
|---|---|---|---|---|---|---|
| 24. | Equipment failure (power tools) | Participant struck by piece of faulty equipment or by rock fragment | - Training in use of tool<br>- Frequent inspection of tools<br>- Safety glasses<br>- Gloves<br>- Other PPE as needed (face guard?)<br>- Hearing protection<br>- Safety briefing<br>- Awareness of location of others<br>- Maintain safe area around person using tool<br>- Change out workers to avoid fatigue | III | D | None |
| 25. | Remote area (medical/ communication) | Consequence of injury escalates because of remoteness | - ERP<br>- Communications equipment<br>- GPS<br>- First Aid training<br>- First Aid kit<br>- Group interactions and assessments<br>- Adequate survival supplies<br>- Medical screening | II | E | None |
| 26. | All other hazards | - Darkness/low light<br>- Strong sunlight<br>- Fire hazard<br>- Smoke/Dust/Fog<br>- Allergens<br>- Bridges/Fences/Utility lines<br>- Fatigue/Dehydration<br>- Food handling<br>- Language/Cultural differences<br>- Pre-existing Physical/ Medical needs<br>- Separation of individuals from group<br>- Lack of rest stops<br>- Individual behaviors/ Risk acceptance | - Standard procedures | IV | D | None |

* All other potential hazards in Hazard Summary assessed as very low potential consequences (Cat IV).

## Activity Detailed Risk Summary 2D

## Activity/School: **Generic Fieldwork on Outcrops**

### Risk Assessment Summary

Activity/School: **Generic Fieldwork**

Field Site: **Water Activities**

| | Hazard Area | Event | Prevention and Mitigation Measures in Place | Con. | Prob. | Extra |
|---|---|---|---|---|---|---|
| 27. | Extreme water temperatures | Participant remains in cold water too long and develops hypothermia | - Strongly recommend eating good meal prior to prolonged exposure to the water<br>- Recommend wearing wetsuit, skin, or long-sleeved T-shirt while in water<br>- Limit time in the water<br>- Safety briefing to include warnings about hypothermia<br>- Swim in teams | IV | D | None |
| 28. | Sharp Objects/ Toxic/Allergic Sources such as:<br><br>*Marine water*—reef organisms, rocks<br><br>*Fresh water*—submerged tree limbs, rocks | Participant strikes or is struck by a sharp object in water resulting in a sting, cut, or blunt trauma | - Safety briefing about marine life and their defense mechanisms including sharp, hard surfaces and chemical toxins<br>- Self identify for allergic reactions; doctor's release on required medical form<br>- Safety briefing about swimming around coral formations and self awareness in water<br>- Recommend using long-sleeved/leg swimwear<br>- Use buddy system<br>- First Aid kit onboard boats<br>- Orientation to local river, stream, lake, or ocean conditions | III | D | None |
| 29. | Strong Sunlight | Participant is exposed all day to direct sun and does not appropriately apply sunscreen cream, thus developing sunburn and possibly sun poisoning | - Safety briefing about excessive sun exposure<br>- Use of PPE including recommended head gear and long-sleeved/leg clothing<br>- First Aid kit and training<br>- Extra sunscreen with activity coordinator | IV | C | None |

## Activity Detailed Risk Summary 2D

### Activity/School: Generic Fieldwork on Outcrops

| | Hazard Area | Event | Prevention and Mitigation Measures in Place | Con. | Prob. | Extra |
|---|---|---|---|---|---|---|
| 30. | Toxic/Allergic Sources<br>• Marine waters: defense toxins<br>• Fresh waters: bacteria, toxins | Participant comes in contact with a toxic source or an allergen resulting in paralysis or an extreme allergic reaction | - First Aid and CPR training<br>- ERP<br>- Pre-activity Orientation | II | E | None |
| 31. | Animals<br>• Marine waters: Barracuda, Sharks<br>• Fresh water: Snakes, Gators, Leeches | Participant comes in contact with an aggressive animal while in the water resulting in an attack, bite, or sting. The event causes excessive bleeding or shock | - Safety briefing about swimming in open ocean and about large fish behavior; dangers of bleeding in ocean<br>- Safety briefing about swimming in designated fresh water environment and what animals to be aware of in that environment<br>- Pre-trip swim/snorkel skills test<br>- Fieldwork team acts as the spotter for one another while conducting in water activities<br>- PFD wear required<br>- First Aid and CPR training<br>- ERP | II | E | None |
| 32. | Swimming, wading, and snorkeling, Water (waves, tides, currents, depth) | Case 1. Participant takes in water through snorkel while swimming in high waves, panics, and submerges and drowns<br><br>Case 2. Participant is not familiar with swimming in deep water (>30 ft), panics, and submerges and drowns<br><br>Case 3. Participant is swept away in current or swiftness of river flow, submerges and drowns | - Daily activity and safety briefings prior to engaging in water activities<br>- Required medical release stating delegate is physically fit<br>- Required swim and snorkel skills test for ocean activities prior to leaving for field area<br>- In water field activities monitored by all members of the fieldwork party<br>- Self-identification for non-participation in any activity<br>- Strategic positioning of boats as boundary markers for snorkeling area<br>- Required buddy system<br>- PFD wear required<br>- First Aid and CPR training<br>- ERP | I | E | None |

## Activity Detailed Risk Summary 2D

### Activity/School: Generic Fieldwork on Outcrops

| | Hazard Area | Event | Prevention and Mitigation Measures in Place | Con. | Prob. | Extra |
|---|---|---|---|---|---|---|
| 33. | Lifting/Carrying | Participant inadvertently submerges while trying to carry heavy equipment to shore resulting in water inhalation | - PFD wear required<br>- Scout route to shore, avoid drop-offs<br>- Proper lifting/carrying/ transfer techniques<br>- Beach/land boat as necessary<br>- Use flotation device for transfer<br>- First Aid and CPR training<br>- ERP<br>- Orientation and fieldwork team support | III | E | None |
| 34. | Fatigue/ Dehydration | Participant does not drink enough fluid throughout the day and expends more energy than normal while swimming and becomes tired and disoriented while in the water, panics, and submerges resulting in drowning | - Daily safety and activity briefing highlighting signs and consequences of dehydration<br>- Field work team will watch for signs of dehydration<br>- Required swim test<br>- Required PFD wear<br>- Required buddy system<br>- Coolers with sufficient drinks aboard each boat or on shore by work party<br>- Maximum 100 m distance from boats during all snorkel stops<br>- Scheduling of stops to preclude overexertion<br>- First Aid and CPR training<br>- ERP | I | E | None |
| 35. | Language Cultural Differences | Participant or buddy pair has English as second language, misunderstands instructions during daily safety and activities briefing, enters water, gets separated from group, becomes distressed, panics, submerges and drowns | - At least one strong English speaker in each pair<br>- Daily safety and activity briefings<br>- Use communication techniques to verify understanding of safety briefings<br>- Field work coordinator make individual contact with non-native speakers to verify understanding<br>- Identify boundaries and out of bounds areas to all participants<br>- Required PFD wear<br>- Required buddy system<br>- ERP<br>- First Aid and CPR training | I | E | None |

## Activity Detailed Risk Summary 2D

Activity/School: **Generic Fieldwork on Outcrops**

| | Hazard Area | Event | Prevention and Mitigation Measures in Place | Con. | Prob. | Extra |
|---|---|---|---|---|---|---|
| 36. | Pre-existing Physical/ Medical Needs | Participant has pre-existing physical condition that is private medical information, participates in an 'in water' activity that exacerbates or re-activates the condition, delegate is distressed, panics, and submerges and drowns | - Required medical release prior to participation<br>- Daily safety and activity briefing<br>- Self-identification for exclusion from activity<br>- Pre-trip notification to field work coordinator regarding pre-existing conditions so that mitigation or special equipment can be secured to achieve safe execution of the activity<br>- Required PFD wear<br>- Buddy system<br>- ERP<br>- First Aid and CPR training | I | E | None |
| 37. | Separation of individuals from Group; Individual behaviors and risk acceptance | Participant or participants decide to venture away from group against instruction, or because of curiosity, trouble is encountered due to high-energy ocean conditions, heavy currents, distance from boats, or animal attack, then one or both is/are distressed, panic, submerge and drown | - Pre trip letter from management<br>- Field work coordinator monitors behavior of participants and make adjustments as required<br>- Required PFD wear<br>- Required buddy system<br>- ERP<br>- First Aid and CPR training | I | E | None |
| 38. | Equipment Failure | Case 1. Participant purchases inferior mask and snorkel, during swimming/snorkel Site, snorkel tube fails and person experiences temporary inability to breathe, panics, submerges and drowns<br><br>Case 2. Delegate punctures inflated PFD in deep water (>5 m), becomes fatigued in return swim to boat, panics, submerges and drowns | - Pre-course instructions include recommendations for equipment standards<br>- Snorkel gear to be evaluated and approved by qualified instructor during snorkel skills test<br>- Required PFD wear<br>- Required buddy system<br>- ERP<br>- First Aid and CPR training | I | E | None |

## Activity Detailed Risk Summary 2D

### Activity/School: **Generic Fieldwork on Outcrops**

| | Hazard Area | Event | Prevention and Mitigation Measures in Place | Con. | Prob. | Extra |
|---|---|---|---|---|---|---|
| 39. | Limited/Remote Medical Services | Participant sustains a non-life threatening injury, but condition worsens due to extended and strenuous transport to medical facility by boat | - ERP<br>- Field First Aid kit and backboard-restraint system onboard<br>- Shock prevention measures<br>- Satellite phone onboard<br>- First Aid and CPR training | II | E | None |
| 40. | Limited Communication | Participant sustains a non-life threatening injury however, there is not cell or Satellite coverage in the area for Emergency response–the condition may worsen due to extended and strenuous transport to medical facility by boat | - ERP<br>- Field first aid kit and backboard/restraint system onboard<br>- First Aid and CPR training<br>- Ship to shore radios<br>- Other backup communication equipment<br>- Maps of cellular/satellite phone coverage | II | E | None |
| 41. | All other in water activities | Minor accidents | - Safety briefings<br>- Emergency Response Plan<br>- First Aid and CPR training<br>- Orientation | IV | D | None |

* All other potential hazards in Hazard Summary assessed as very low potential consequences (Cat IV).

## RISK ASSESSMENT PROCESS DESCRIPTION AND CHARTER *for Name of Field Activity*

### INTRODUCTION

This document describes the process for conducting a Risk Assessment (RA) for Field Activities. It is also designed to be used as a sample Charter for conducting such risk assessments, modified as appropriate for your organization and activity. Risk assessments are conducted to identify the significant risks associated with these activities and ensure that they are appropriately managed, in accordance with requirements of the organization's safety program.

The Risk Assessment Team (RA Team) for ***the Field Activity*** consists of the Activity coordinator(s), selected instructors, at least one outside person (not involved with conducting the Activity) that has training and experience in risk assessment, and others as appropriate. RA Team members evaluate the hazards associated with ***the Field Activity*** and estimate risk probabilities and consequences using the Field Activity Risk Matrix (form 2A, above; this matrix is to be used for risk assessments of all Field Activities to ensure consistency of assessment of similar field activities across various groups within the organization). As necessary, risk-management alternatives are identified and evaluated. The team then prepares a *Field Activity Risk Assessment Summary Report* (RASR; form 2D, above) summarizing the risk level, key findings, and recommendations. The RASR is reviewed and approved by a level of management/supervisor/peer appropriate for the assessed level of risk. The approved RASR forms the basis for subsequent preparations for the safe conduct of the Activity.

### PURPOSE AND OBJECTIVES

#### Purpose

The purpose of the risk assessment is to identify the significant risks associated with ***the Field Activity***, and to identify prevention and mitigation measures to be implemented.

#### Objectives

- Understand current risks of ***the Field Activity*** and existing controls for managing the risks.
- Identify opportunities for additional or enhanced prevention and mitigation measures.
- Prepare recommendations for ongoing risk management.

### PRODUCTS

#### Primary Products:

A ***Field Activity Risk Assessment Summary Report*** (form 2A, above) that includes risks, consequences, and risk management procedures:

1) A summary description of scenarios evaluated.
2) A Risk Matrix for ***the Field Activity*** containing scenarios evaluated (Figure 2).
3) Recommended prevention and mitigation measures for each hazard or scenario.
4) Issues and risks reviewed by the RA Team and documentation of the analysis and results.
5) A summary of identified risks for review and approval by the Activity Staff and appropriate level of Management. (This varies by organization. In typical commercial enterprises, progressively higher levels of management approval are required for progressively higher risk categories. Table 3 provides a placeholder with common terms for management levels than can be modified for a particular organization.)

**Table 3.** Approval levels by risk category.

| Risk Category* | Approval Level |
|---|---|
| All Lower Risks | First-line: Supervisor |
| All Intermediate Risks | Second-level: Manager |
| Higher Risks | Third-level: Vice President |

**After prevention and mitigation measures are implemented.*

#### Secondary Products

1) Important safety concerns identified which are outside the scope of the risk assessment.
2) Feedback on the risk assessment process.

### PROCESS

#### Pre-Activity Planning

1) Activity Owner selects RA Team members in consultation with the Activity Coordinator. Team members attend risk assessment training (approximately 16-hour course), as needed. **A minimum of one person on team must have RA training**

**and experience in conducting risk assessments.** Recommended people to include on the RA Team are:
- Activity Coordinator and Instructors *(Names: ________________)*
- SHE Advisor/Safety Group contact *(Name: ________________)*
- Others as appropriate (e.g. Geoscience Field Safety Coordinator) *(Names: ______________)*

2) Familiarization: Review planned activities, available data and organization experience on planned or similar activities, and visit field locations, and interview experts, as required. See the ***Preparation Checklist for Risk Assessment of Field Activity*** (form 2C, above) for guidance in assembling information and materials for conducting the risk assessment.

## Assessment Activities (Completed by RA team)

### For *New* Field School or Field Trip:

1) Review the ***Risk Management Summary Report: Generic Field Work and Field Activity Potential Hazards Register*** (forms 2D and 2B, above), along with the materials listed on the **Preparation Checklist for Risk Assessment of Field Activity** (form 2C, above).
2) Determine which hazards are present at each field site or in common activities (e.g. driving, boating) that could pose a significant threat to safety, health, or the environment in terms of consequences or probability of occurrence. Use a copy of the ***Field Activity Potential Hazards Register*** for each field site or common activity. This register is designed to aid thoroughness and consistency of assessment and documentation. (See detailed information on the ***Field Activity Potential Hazards Register*** for guidance.) We recommend starting with most hazardous common activities first (such as driving); then assess field sites in order of course delivery, to highlight dependant or cumulative hazards, such as fatigue factors and sunlight exposure whose hazard level can depend on time of day or level of intensity of previous activities during the day or preceding days.
3) Determine prevention and mitigation measures to be applied and document on ***Risk Assessment Summary Report.***
4) Develop credible* scenarios based on significant hazards identified to understand range of potential consequences. (*Reasonably likely behaviors or situations that involve a significant health, safety, or environmental risk to personnel, property, or both.)

> NOTE: **Credible scenarios should also include situations where safety measures are ignored or fail to function properly.**

5) Determine the probability and consequence of each scenario with identified prevention and mitigation measures in place and plot it on the ***Field Activity Risk Matrix*** (See notes on the matrix page for probability interpretations).
6) Consider additional prevention and mitigation measures after reviewing the cumulative risk level of the activities as a whole (as necessary).
7) Document assessment results on ***Field Activity Risk Assessment Summary Report*** (form 2A, above).

> NOTE: **The overall Activity Risk Level of the Activity is the highest level of any individual scenario.**

### If Field School or Field Trip with Existing Risk Assessment:

Review existing Risk Assessment for completeness and accuracy, using data and organizational experience from previous sessions or similar activities along with any new information on field-site conditions. Add or modify scenarios as appropriate and plot on risk matrix. Document on ***Field Activity Risk Assessment Summary Report.***

### If Field Work:

Review ***Risk Management Summary Report: Generic Field Work*** (form 2D, above). Using the ***Field Activity Potential Hazards Register*** identify new or different levels of hazards, and associated risks and proposed safeguards. Develop **credible** scenarios for new or changed hazards. Plot new risk scenarios on Risk Matrix. Modify overall Risk Level for ***the Field Activity*** as appropriate. Obtain management approval for the Activity if the modified Risk Level increases.

### Follow-up Activities

For RA Team:

- Review draft *Field Activity Risk Assessment Summary Report* with ________ (appropriate management; see Table 3 above).
- Finalize report.
- Have appropriate level of management approve risk (consistent with safety program requirements; see Table 3 above).

For Activity Owner

- Communicate the Risk Assessment findings and resolution plans to those affected by the assessment (starting with the Activity Staff).
- Ensure closure of any action items identified in Risk Assessment.

## BOUNDARIES (FOR RA TEAM ACTIVITIES)

### Areas for Review

- *[The Field Activity]* led or sponsored by ________ (organizational unit).

### Risk Consequences of Interest

- Safety, Health, Environmental
- Public Disruption, Media Impact

### Areas to be Addressed

- Transportation (e.g. driving, aircraft, watercraft)
- Field activities (e.g. climbing, hiking, swimming, etc.)

### Human Factors Considerations

- Human error, language and communications challenges, and differing attitudes and cultures must be considered in the evaluation of risk scenarios.
- Field activities (e.g. climbing, hiking, exposure to heat or cold, etc.)
- Physical capabilities (fitness, limited mobility or sensorium, fatigue, etc.)

## FEEDBACK

Participant feedback and Safety Log information from previous Activities should be used as input into the risk assessment

## TIME FRAME

The ***Field Activity Risk Assessment Summary Report*** is to be completed by *(fill in the date)*. The **Field Activity Risk Assessment Summary Report** is to be approved by management sponsor by (fill in the date).

*Experience to date indicates the following typical time expenditures for conducting or reviewing the base Risk Assessments:*

| | | |
|---|---|---|
| *–**Field Work:*** | *1–2 hours* | *(to review and modify existing RA)* |
| *–**Existing Schools:*** | *1–2 hours* | *(to review and modify existing RA)* |
| *–**New Schools/Trips:*** | *8–16 hours* | *(to construct new RA of all new sites; less time is required if sites already assessed for other school or trip and in Field Safety Library*)* |

**Field Safety Library is an organization-wide compilation of Risk Assessment and SHE documents for Field Activities. At ExxonMobil, these materials are kept in a central electronic repository available on line. In addition, completed **Site Safety Summary Sheets** (form 3K, in Section 3) can be searched by geographic location (country, state, latitude, longitude) to leverage worldwide experience.*

## POTENTIAL HAZARDS SAFETY GUIDELINES–EXAMPLES

### Perspective Check:

- Odds of winning top prize in state lottery: 1 in 135,000,000.
- Odds of dying in automobile accident (per year in the U.S.A.): 1 in 6000.
- Odds of dying of injuries sustained by falling out of bed: 1 in 13

### Natural Environment:

*Uneven/Slippery Walking Surfaces*

Probability/Consequence:
- Slips, trips, and falls (indoor and outdoor) contribute to 13,162 fatalities per year in the U.S.A.

Key Contributing Factors:
- Loose rocks, scree slopes, talus blocks
- Inattention to foot placement
- Overestimating personal ability/fitness

- Underestimating effects of rain, snow, mist, plant growth on sliperiness
- Inappropriate foot gear, especially soles

Prevention and Mitigation:
- Wear appropriate foot gear with good-traction soles (Vibram-type)
- Use hiking staff/trekking poles as appropriate (beware of environmental impact of poles on soils and soft ground).
- Watch where you place your feet
- Never step ON anything you can step OVER, never step OVER anything you can step AROUND
- On slopes, place entire foot on ground where possible, remaining upright directly over your feet
- Going downhill, take short steps and keep your knees flexed. Side step down particularly loose slopes.

References:
- Boy Scout Handbook
- The Dayhiker's Handbook

*Foul Weather Considerations—wind, rain, snow, lightning, and flash floods*

Lightning:

Probability/Consequence:
- Lightning injures around 400 and kills 73 people per year in the U.S.A.

Key Contributing Factors:
- Lack of prompt action to protect their lives, property and the lives of others
- Lack of appreciation of all the dangers associated with thunderstorms and lightning
- Lack of awareness of current and forecast weather conditions
- Lack of awareness of local weather patterns (afternoon buildups, frontal storms, etc.)
- Inability to see/sense approaching thunderstorms due to topography

Prevention and Mitigation:
- The 30-30 Rule: Use the 30-30 rule where visibility is good and there is nothing obstructing your view of the thunderstorm. When you see lightning, count the time until you hear thunder. If that time is 30 seconds or less, the thunderstorm is within 6 miles of you and is dangerous. Seek shelter immediately. The threat of lightning continues for much longer period than most people realize. Wait at least 30 minutes after the last clap of thunder before leaving shelter. Don't be fooled by sunshine or blue sky! Watch where you place your feet.
- In areas with limited visibility to all points of the horizon, use a Lightning Detector. Discontinue field activities when detector indicates an approaching storm within 6 miles of your position and implement your storm evacuation plan.
- **Postpone activities promptly.** Don't wait for rain. Go quickly inside a completely enclosed building, not a carport, open garage or covered patio. If no enclosed building is convenient, get inside a hard-topped all-metal vehicle. The steel frame of the vehicle provides some protection if you are not touching metal. A cave is a good option outside but move as far as possible from the cave entrance.
- **Be the lowest point.** Lightning hits the tallest object. In the mountains if you are above treeline, you ARE the highest object around. Quickly get below treeline and get into a grove of small trees. Don't be the second tallest object during a lightning storm! Crouch down if you are in an exposed area.
- **Keep an eye on the sky.** Look for darkening skies, flashes of lightning, or increasing wind, which may be signs of an approaching thunderstorm.
- **Listen for the sound of thunder.** If you can hear thunder, go to a safe shelter immediately.
- **If you can't get to a shelter, stay away from trees.** If there is no shelter, crouch in the open, keeping twice as far away from a tree as it is tall.
- **Avoid metal!** Drop metal-framed backpacks, stay away from clothes lines, fences, exposed sheds and electrically conductive elevated objects. Don't hold on to metal items such as tools and hiking staffs. Large metal objects can conduct lightning. Small metal objects can cause burns.
- **Move away from a group of people.** Stay several yards away from other people. Don't huddle in a group.
- **Get out of the water.** It's a great conductor of electricity. Stay off the beach and out of small boats or canoes. If caught in a boat, crouch down in the center of the boat away from metal hardware. Swimming, wading, snorkeling and scuba diving are NOT safe. Lightning can strike the water and travel some distance beneath and away from its point of contact. Don't stand in puddles of water, even if wearing rubber boots.

References:
- NOAA/National Weather Service http://www.lightningsafety.noaa.gov/)
- ARC/FEMA/National Weather Service hazardous weather brochures.

Flash Flood:

Probability/Consequence:

- Flash floods kill 135 people per year in the U.S.A., most of whom intentionally drive into rising waters

Key Contributing Factors:

- Lack of appreciation of the power of moving water and how fast it can rise
- Lack of prompt action to protect their lives, property and the lives of others
- Lack of awareness of current and forecast weather conditions
- Lack of awareness of local weather patterns (afternoon buildups, frontal storms, etc.)
- Inability to see/sense approaching thunderstorms due to topography

Prevention and Mitigation:

- Check the weather forecast. Monitor sky and NOAA weather radio
- Don't park vehicles in a dry wash or near a stream during threatening weather conditions.
- Know where high ground is and how to get there quickly.
- Never try to walk or swim through swiftly moving water.
- Never try to cross water in a vehicle, whether it is moving or not.
- If your vehicle stalls in rapidly rising water, abandon it immediately and move to higher ground.
- Listen for distant thunder. Runoff from a faraway storm may be headed your way.
- Remember that flash flooding can occur up to 12 hours after a heavy rain event.

References:

- NOAA/National Weather Service http://www.crh.noaa.gov/unr/edusafe/swaw/flash_flood_safety.htm)
- ARC/FEMA/National Weather Service hazardous weather brochures.

Animals—Insects, Reptiles, Mammals, Other:

Probability/Consequence:

- Contact with venomous animals and plants contributes to about 300,000 injuries and 66 fatalities per year in the U.S.A. (one-year fatality odds: 1 in 4,472,459)
- Bitten or struck by dog or other mammal contributes to 94 fatalities per year in the U.S.A. (one-year odds: 1 in 14,866,713)
- Bitten or stung by nonvenomous insect and other arthropods contributes to 10 fatalities per year in the U.S.A. (one-year fatality odds: 1 in 27,282,000)

Key Contributing Factors:

- Harassing, handling wildlife—more than 40% of all bites are not accidental
- Lack of awareness of habits and habitats of wildlife

Prevention and Mitigation:

- Watch where you place your hands and feet
- Wear gloves, long pants, and high-top boots/snake gaiters as appropriate
- Shake out clothing, gloves, boots before donning, especially in the morning.

References:

- Management of Wilderness and Environmental Emergencies, 2nd edition, Auerbach, P. S., and E. C. Geehr, editors, 1989, C.V. Mosby, St Louis, Missouri.

## Human Factors/Participant Activities:

### *Hiking/Walking:*

Probability/Consequence:

- Slips, trips, and falls (indoor and outdoor) contribute to 13,162 fatalities per year in the U.S.A.

Key Contributing Factors:

- Loose rocks, scree slopes, talus blocks
- Inattention to foot placement
- Overestimating personal ability/fitness, resulting fatigue
- Underestimating effects of rain, snow, mist, plant growth on slipperiness
- Inappropriate foot gear, especially soles

Prevention and Mitigation:

- Wear appropriate foot gear with good-traction soles (Vibram-type)
- Watch where you place your feet
- Never step ON anything you can step OVER, never step OVER anything you can step AROUND
- On a continuous hike, stop for 5-minute rest with legs up every 45–60 minutes

References:

- Boy Scout Handbook

# 3 Planning & Preparation

Risk Assessment Process

Planning and Preparation

Pre-Activity Safety Review

Field Operations

Post-Activity Learning

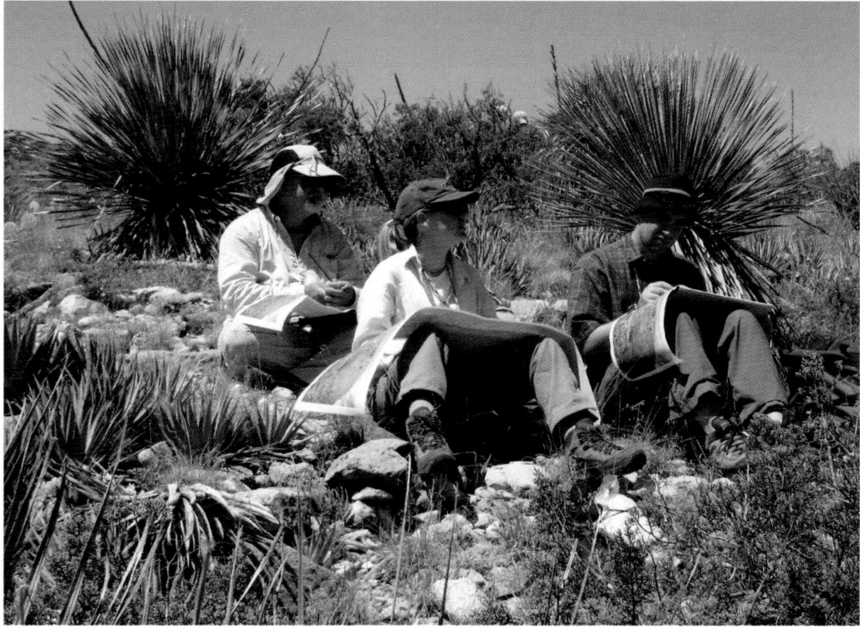

# SECTION 3

## Planning and Preparation

The key to the safe and successful execution of any Field Activity is in the planning and preparation. This section describes the processes to be followed in preparation for any Field Activity, specifically related to Safety and Health preparedness. It is organized roughly in chronological order, with references to related procedures and examples of documentation provided where appropriate.

Once the Activity Staff has been selected, the Activity Coordinator should organize an initial planning meeting as soon as practical. A primary objective of the initial meeting should be to identify all pre-Activity actions that need to be taken and assign Staff responsibilities for completing them. In this and subsequent sessions, the following issues must be addressed. The general flow of actions for all field activities is outlined below and elaborated in following sections.

**3.1 ACTIVITY STAFF**

General Staff Selection
Additional Considerations
Safety Watch

**3.2 STAFF SAFETY, HEALTH, AND ENVIRONMENTAL (SHE) RELATED TRAINING**

Required Training for All Staff
Training for Special Activities
Training Waiver

**3.3 MATERIALS AND EQUIPMENT**

**3.4 EMERGENCY RESPONSE PLAN (ERP)**

ERP Contents
Field Schools and Field Trips
Activities in Foreign Countries

**3.5 COMMUNICATIONS WITH PARTICIPANTS**

Pre-Activity Package to Participants
- Safety Assessment
- Management Letter
- Participant Information Forms

Information from Participants

**3.6 SAFETY, HEALTH, AND ENVIRONMENT (SHE) PLAN DEVELOPMENT**

**3.7 FIELD ACTIVITIES OPERATED BY OTHERS (OBO)**

**OBO Field Trips—see Section 3.7 (*typically takes 1 hour*):**
- □ Complete Potential Hazard Register.
- □ Complete Personal Safety Plan.
- □ Fill out personal Emergency Medical Information card.
- □ Discuss preparations with supervisor and obtain endorsement on Personal Safety Plan.


DOI:10.1306/1119799DEG3223

**Fieldwork (small groups, experienced workers) (*typically takes 1–2 hours*):**

- ☐ Notify Geoscience Field Safety Coordinator of the planned activity to reserve safety equipment and schedule pre-trip review.
- ☐ Review roles and responsibilities of all staff positions and their SHE training status.
- ☐ Review existing Generic Fieldwork Risk Assessment using Hazard Register, modify if necessary.
- ☐ Complete Emergency Information and Medical Certification form, submit to activity coordinator.
- ☐ Determine communications capabilities (i.e., cell-phone/radio coverage) and address needs.
- ☐ Develop a Field Activity SHE Plan, including Emergency Response Plan (use checklist with the SHE Plan in Section 3.6).
- ☐ Conduct a Pre-Activity Safety Review Meeting with Owner, obtain endorsement at least 1 week before.
- ☐ IF applicable:
    - ☐ *Review host organization SHE Plan and develop bridging document or develop original SHE Plan*
    - ☐ *Non-scheduled/Charter transportation approval (process varies by organization)*
    - ☐ *Foreign Travel approval (process varies by organization)*

**Field Schools (recurrent events, moderate-sized groups, less experienced) (*typically takes 2–3 hours with existing Risk Assessment available*):**

- ☐ Designate a Training Contact. This person will work with the Staff to coordinate the assembly of materials to be sent to Participants. He or she will also handle the responses from Participants and deliver the appropriate materials to the Coordinator. The Activity Coordinator may serve in this role.
- ☐ Notify the Geoscience Field Safety Coordinator (GFSC) of the planned activity to reserve safety equipment and schedule pre-trip review.
- ☐ Review existing Risk Assessment and Site Specific Summary sheets, upgrade as necessary. **Remember that alternate sites must be identified, assessed, and approved prior to beginning the Activity. Visits to unapproved sites are not permitted.**
- ☐ Select Staff, review their SHE training status *(CPR, First Aid, Defensive Driving, Field Safety Leadership).*
- ☐ Review roles and responsibilities for all staff positions.
- ☐ Review content and delivery of Safety Briefings—who will deliver, how to deliver them, when/where they will be delivered, and how to check for understanding.
- ☐ Determine vehicle needs and preliminary selection of drivers (among Staff).
- ☐ Prepare and send out pre-school information package to participants.
- ☐ Review and address Participants' special needs.
- ☐ Determine communications capabilities (i.e. cell phone coverage) and address needs.
- ☐ Determine safety equipment and PPE required for the Activity and review Safety Watch pack basic contents and determine need for supplementing. Reserve with the GFSC or other source.
- ☐ Develop a Field Activity SHE Plan, including Emergency Response Plan (use checklist on front page of SHE Plan). Recommend doing as a team about 4 weeks before class.
- ☐ Obtain field safety gear from Geoscience Field Safety Coordinator or other source.
- ☐ Conduct a Pre-Activity Safety Review Meeting with Activity Owner and obtain endorsement (no later than 2 weeks before start of School).
- ☐ IF applicable:
    - ☐ *Non-scheduled/Charter transportation approval (process varies by organization)*
    - ☐ *Foreign Travel approval (varies by organization)*

**Field Trips (one-time events, large groups, wide range of experience) (*typically takes 8–16 hours*):**

- ☐ Notify the Geoscience Field Safety Coordinator (GFSC) of the planned activity to reserve safety equipment and schedule pre-trip review.
- ☐ Conduct Risk Assessment using standard process, using Standard Hazard Registers.
- ☐ Construct Site Specific Summary sheets for each field stop. **Remember that alternate sites must be identified, assessed, and approved prior to beginning the Activity. Visits to unapproved sites are not allowed under this process.**
- ☐ Select Staff, review their SHE training status (CPR, First Aid, Defensive Driving, Field Safety Leadership).
- ☐ Review roles and responsibilities for all staff positions.
- ☐ Review content and delivery of Safety Briefings—who will deliver, how to deliver them and how to check for understanding, etc.
- ☐ Determine vehicle needs and make preliminary selection of drivers (from the Staff).
- ☐ Prepare and send out pre-trip information package to participants (by trip coordinator).
- ☐ Review and address Participants' special needs.
- ☐ Determine communications capabilities, i.e. cell phone coverage (Section 3)
- ☐ Develop a Field Activity SHE Plan, including Emergency Response Plan (use checklist on front page). Recommend doing as a team about 4 weeks before class.
- ☐ Obtain field safety gear from Geoscience Field Safety Coordinator or other source.
- ☐ Conduct a Pre-Activity Safety Review Meeting with Activity Owner and obtain endorsement (no later than 2 weeks before start of School).
- ☐ IF applicable:
    - ☐ *Review host SHE Plan and develop bridging document or develop original SHE Plan*
    - ☐ *Non-scheduled/Charter transportation approval (process varies by organization)*
    - ☐ *Foreign Travel approval (varies by organization)*

**For all Field Activities:**

- ☐ Complete Field Activity Follow-up Report within 2 weeks of return and forward to Geoscience Field Safety Coordinator.

**General time line of activities associated with a particular instance of a Field Activity**

*Weeks:*

| 1 | 2 | 3 | 4 | 5 | 6 | 7 | 8 | 9 | 10 | 11 | 12 | 13 | 14 | 15 | 16 |
|---|---|---|---|---|---|---|---|---|---|---|---|---|---|---|---|

Construct or Review Base RA

Prepare Precourse Materials and Send to Participants

*<4–8 weeks>*
Receive responses from participants, make modifications as required, finalize SHE and ERP plans

Pre-Trip Safety Review
⇦≥2 weeks before⇨

Finalize Preparations

Conduct field activity

*<2 weeks>*
Complete Follow-Up Report

| 1 | 2 | 3 | 4 | 5 | 6 | 7 | 8 | 9 | 10 | 11 | 12 | 13 | 14 | 15 | 16 |
|---|---|---|---|---|---|---|---|---|---|---|---|---|---|---|---|

**General time line during Field Activity**

*Days of field activity:*

| 1 | 2 | 3 | 4 | 5 | 6 | 7 | 8 | 9 | 10 | 11 | 12 | 13 | N |
|---|---|---|---|---|---|---|---|---|---|---|---|---|---|

Initial Orientation and Safety Briefing

Start-of-Day Safety Briefings

Site Safety Briefings

End-of-Day Safety Debriefing (with Staff)

Final Safety Debriefing with entire group

*≤30 min* | *5 minutes each* | *≤30 min*

## SECTION 3.1: STAFF SELECTION

### Staff Selection–General Remarks

> NOTE: Whenever possible, the Activity Staff should be selected prior to conducting the Risk Assessment review described in Section 1.

The Activity Owner and the Activity Coordinator will work together to identify the additional Activity Staff. The prescribed total number of staff should be determined by referring to the attached Staff/Participant Ratio Guidelines (see form 3A, below). If the Activity can be safely and efficiently executed with a smaller staff, or if staff availability is an issue, deviation from the ratio guidelines can be pursued by submitting a Waiver Approval Form to the Activity Owner.

> NOTE: Operating an Activity with a reduced number of Staff requires the identification of one or more qualified Participant(s) (SHE trained) to fill Staff roles in the event of an emergency. Pre-Activity agreement by the selected Participant(s) should be documented. SHE training includes First Aid, CPR, Defensive Driving, Field Safety Leadership (see Section 3.6).

**Instructors:** Activity Instructors should be selected based on technical expertise, instructional experience, SHE training and experience, and availability.

**Logistics Coordinators:** Logistics Coordinators should be selected based on experience, SHE training and experience, and availability.

## Additional Considerations:

**Overall Staff Experience**—Do not staff with too many persons with little experience. Although the only way to gain experience is through participation in activities, consider trying to break-in new Staff on less challenging activities, i.e. instructional sessions that are physically less demanding or that have smaller staff–participant ratios.

**Schedules**—Review what the proposed Staff has planned immediately before and after the planned Activity. For example, do not schedule an Instructor or Logistics Coordinator for a 2-week Activity within a week after or before another similar Activity. Cumulative fatigue could become an issue, reducing their effectiveness. For Logistics Coordinators, the reasoning is more obvious—they will need to be heavily involved in preparations in the period immediately preceding the Activity.

**Overall Staff Compatibility**—Schedule people who will get along well and work together. Intra-Staff conflicts could affect the overall safety of the Activity as well as participant attitudes.

## Safety Watch (Field Schools, Field Trips, Fieldwork)

For every field stop or site visited during a Field School, Field Trip, or Fieldwork, one of the Staff will be designated as the Safety Watch. This should be a **mandatory requirement** that cannot be waived. The Safety Watch will be responsible for monitoring the safety of the day's and site's activities to help ensure their safe execution. For Schools and Trips, the Safety Watch will have no teaching or training duties during class movements. She or he may join in discussions when the participants are safely situated and working on exercises. He or she is the custodian of the Safety Watch Pack (distinctively colored, that uniquely identifies the Safety Watch person—definition and contents in Section 3.3) and is responsible for providing initial first aid in the event of an injury or illness. A complete definition of the role and responsibilities of the Safety Watch is attached (see form 3D, below).

**The following forms for this section are also located on the CD-Rom accompanying this book:**

**Staff/Participation Ratio Guidelines and Roles and Responsibilities—3A**

**Waiver Approval Form—3B**

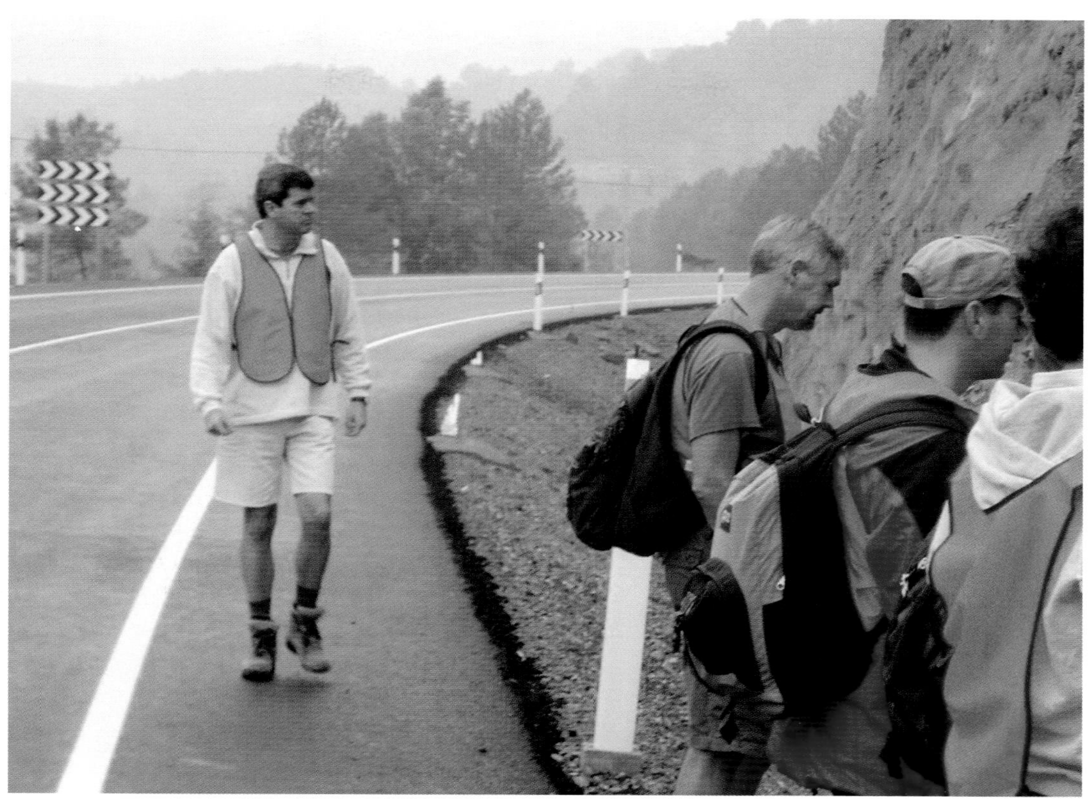

# Staff Responsibilities and Staff—Participant Ratio Guidelines

1. Should be based on Risk Assessment
2. Should have required minimum number of staff
3. Should have sufficient people to cover standard staff positions with the defined responsibilities:

   **Lead Instructor**

   Coordinates overall activity, safety, and emergency response

   Stays out in front of all groups during movements ("on point")

   **Safety Watch**

   Maintains safety watch, enforces safety rules, keep trip safety log

   Carries outcrop safety, communications, and response equipment

   Stays at rear of group during movements ("at sweep")

   Provides initial first aid in event of emergency

   **Assistant Instructor**

   Assists with technical training and safe conduct

   Stays in the middle of the class during movement

   Assembles and directs uninvolved class groups in event of emergency

   **Logistics Coordinator**

   Assists with safe conduct and general health and condition of class

   Issues safety equipment to participants as needed (vests, hard hats, etc.)

   Deploys traffic control devices at roadside stops as required

   Works with Assistant Instructor to manage uninvolved groups during emergency

   Normally remains near parked vehicles for security and as safety watch for participants who may remain in parking area.
4. Participants should be assigned and operate in groups of 3 or 4
5. Generally recommend that Safety Watch come from the ranks of instructors

   Better buy-in and safety awareness among all instructors

   Instructors are more experienced with operating in outcrop environment

   Better alignment with company safety approach and operations

   Excellent experience for "instructors-in-training"

   Can join in technical discussions once the group is in a stationary position.

## Minimum Ratios of Staff to Participants for Field Schools and Field Trips:

| Non-staff Participants | Activity Risk Level* | Instructors | Safety Watch | Logistics Coordinator | Total Staff |
|---|---|---|---|---|---|
| < 7 | L† | *Follow Risk Analysis and Field Procedures for Field Work* | | | |
| 8-16 | L | 1** | 1 | 0/1 | 2/3 |
| 17-24 | L | 2 | 1 | 1 | 4 |
| 25-32 | L | 2 | 2 | 1 | 5 |
| 33-40 | L | 3 | 2 | 1 | 6 |
| **> 40** | **L** | **NOT RECOMMENDED** | | | |
| 0-10 | I‡ | 2 | 1 | 1 | 4 |
| 11-20 | I | 2 | 2 | 1 | 5 |
| **> 20** | **I** | **NOT RECOMMENDED** | | | |
| **> 0** | **H** | **NOT RECOMMENDED** | | | |

* L = lower risk, I = intermediate/moderate risk, H = higher risk.

** Pre-select one participant with appropriate FA/CPR training to perform duties of the Assistant Instructor in case of an emergency.

† *Organize participants in Groups of 3 to 4 people.*

‡ *Organize participants in "Buddy Pairs".*

## Field Activity Safety Process 3B

# Waiver Approval Form

*This form is to be used to request approval to waive Staff Training requirements and/or Staff Participant ratio guidelines.*

Activity: ______________________________ Dates: __________

Activity Type: ______________ Number of Staff: ________ Number of Participants: ________
(School, work, trip, excursion)

## Training Waiver Request

Staff Member: ______________ Activity Position: ______________ Safety Watch (y/n)? _____

Training to be waived: ______________ Reason: ______________

Date last taken: ______________ Date Scheduled to Take: ______________

Risk Mitigating Factors: ______________________________

Additional Justification: ______________________________

### Comments and Approval:

Activity Owner Comments:

Activity Owner Signature: ______________________________ Date: __________

Printed Name: ______________________________

## Staff–Participant Ratio Waiver Request

| | Instructors | Safety Watch | Logistics Coordinator | Total Staff |
|---|---|---|---|---|
| Prescribed Staff per Guidelines: | | | | |
| Proposed Activity Staff: | | | | |

Risk Mitigating Factors:

______________________________

Additional Justification: ______________________________

List the **appropriately trained Participant(s) who have agreed** to perform the duties of the absent staff in case of an emergency. ______________________________

### Comments and Approval:

Activity Owner Comments:

Activity Owner Signature: ______________________________ Date: __________

Printed Name: ______________________________

## SECTION 3.2: STAFF TRAINING

### Required Staff Training

All Activity Staff are required to have certain SHE-related training updated at the intervals noted (Table 4). The types and levels of training required for activity staff is determined by the hazards identified in the Risk Assessment, access to assistance in field locations, and applicable governmental regulations. The sponsoring organization sets the requirements and acceptable equivalent training. The courses listed as required in the table below represent a reasonable minimum level for all field activities. Certification at higher levels of CPR and First Aid may be an acceptable substitute if that training covers delayed-help or wilderness situations.

Solicit updates from the Activity Staff to confirm that their training is up-to-date. Enter this information on the SHE Plan.

### Special Activities Training

For certain Activities, some or all Staff members will be required to obtain additional specialized training. Table 4 identifies some training that could be required. The Activity Coordinator should work with the Geoscience FSC to determine whether specialized training is required for the Activity being planned.

### Training Waiver

If for some reason one or more of the selected Staff is unable to have his or her required training updated in time for the Activity, a waiver for that Activity instance can be requested from the Activity Owner or appropriate level of management (see form 3B, above).

**The following form for this section is also located on the CD-Rom accompanying this book:**
**Field Safety Leadership Curriculum—3C**

## SECTION 3.3: MATERIALS AND EQUIPMENT

Although training and common sense are the most important factors contributing to safe field activities, appropriate materials and equipment greatly enhance safe operations and emergency response. Materials and equipment needs will vary by Activity. Exercise care in selecting the right amount of quality equipment and materials.

NOTE: **Always check the condition and operation of all gear before departing for the field.**

*(text continues on page 63)*

**Table 4.** Example training requirements.

| Required Staff Training | Level | Renewal |
|---|---|---|
| a) CPR, Adult (ARC Adult CPR or equivalent) | 4–6 hours | 1 year |
| b) First Aid (ARC Standard or equivalent) **AND** | 4–6 hours | 3 years |
| Field First Aid (ARC "When Help is Delayed") **OR** | 2 hours | 3 years |
| ARC Wilderness First Aid | 16 hours | 3 years |
| c) Defensive Driving (State-approved course) | 8 hours | 3 years |
| d) Field Safety Leadership (see form 3C, below, for Lesson Plan and Agenda) | 8–16 hours | 4 years |
| **Staff Training—Special Activities** | **Level** | **Renewal** |
| e) Water Safety/Lifesaving (e.g., ARC "Basic Water Safety and Rescue" ) | 6–8 hours | 3 years |
| f) Small Craft Safety (e.g., BSA "Safety Afloat") | | |
| g) Climatic Hazards (Arctic, tropics, desert, etc.) | | |
| h) Power Tools/Special Equipment (specify) | | |
| i) Other—(specify) | | |

*ARC = American Red Cross, BSA = Boy Scouts of America.*

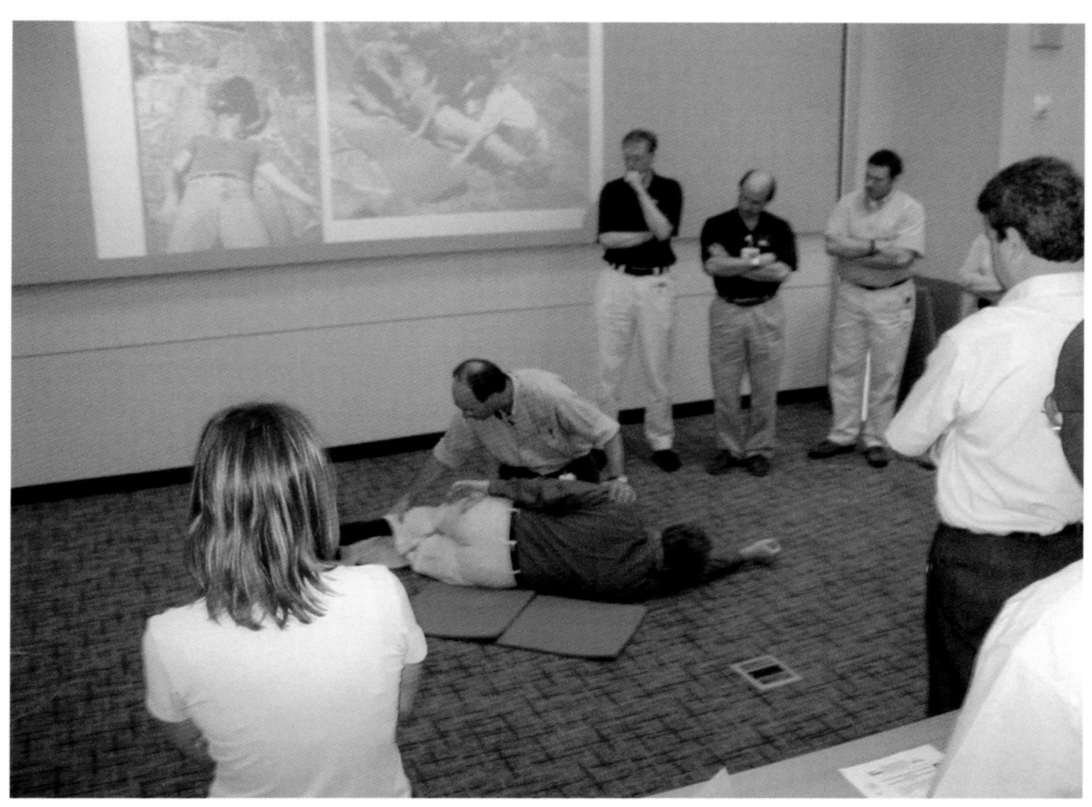

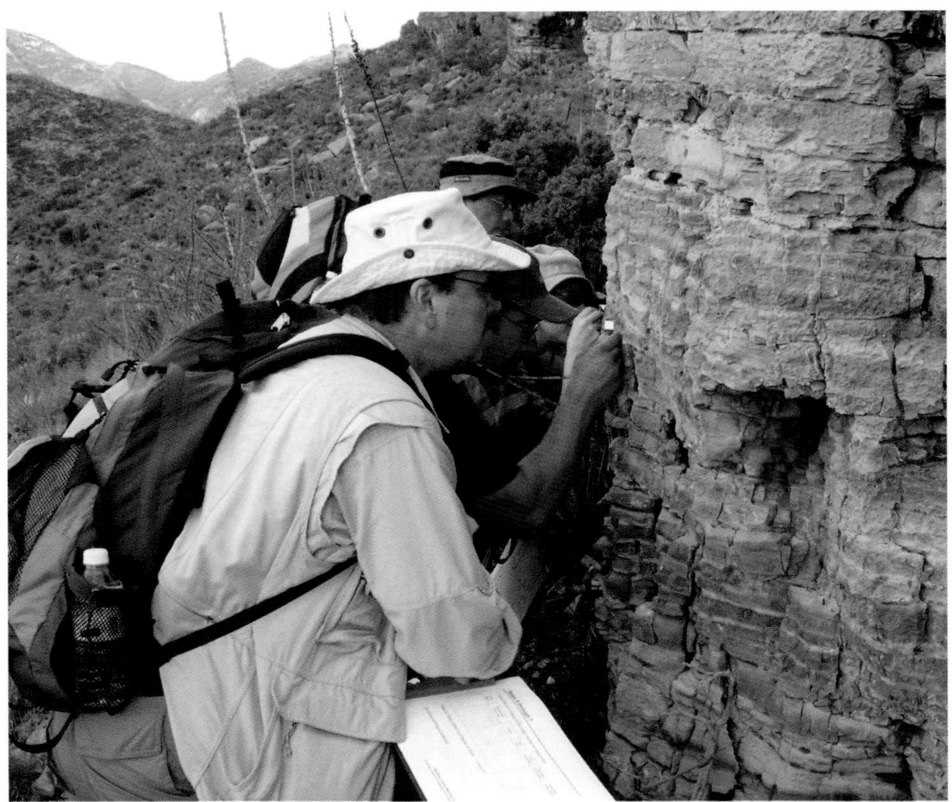

Field Activity Safety Manual 3C

# Suggested Agenda for a Field Safety Leadership School

## Pre-School Actions:

- ► Send out standard pre-trip field package to participants
- ► Create site summary sheets for the two stops
- ► Construct risk assessment (including Hazard Register)
- ► SHE\ERP including management review and endorsement meeting

**Goal:** Acquire and practice strategies to prepare for and conduct safe and effective field activities.

**Learning Objectives:**

Upon completion of this course, you should be able to:

Describe the roles and responsibilities of Activity Staff in preparing for, planning, and conducting safe and effective field activities (Activity Coordinator, Lead Instructor, Safety Watch, Assistant Instructor).

List the three main factors that intersect in causing field emergencies.

Describe how participants' perception of risk affects their attitudes and behaviors in the field.

List key attributes of an effective instructor who promotes field safety.

List the most significant hazards in a typical land-based field school (in terms of consequence or probability).

Describe how to apply the Emergency Action Steps in a delayed-help situation.

Make and execute a plan for responding to an emergency in the field (Check, Call, Care).

Demonstrate the steps in bleeding control (direct pressure, elevation, pressure points, tourniquet).

Demonstrate how to provide in-line stabilization for a victim with a head, neck, or back injury.

Demonstrate or describe how to move a victim in case of immediate danger.

List and describe the 5 main steps of the Field Safety Process.

Describe the main SOPs for driving and hiking and when to apply them.

Demonstrate or describe the use of key pieces of field safety equipment (PPE, communicators, hazard warning, first aid).

Conduct field safety briefings using standard slide templates, site safety summary sheets, participant feedback, and Safety Logbook.

Lead a field stop following the standard operating procedures (including site safety briefing, use of PPE and safety equipment, and documentation in Safety Logbook).

Demonstrate or describe how to evaluate groups and individuals for unsafe or risky behavior and how to intervene effectively.

Demonstrate how to respond to an emergency in the field, including field actions, notifications, and reporting.

# Field Activity Safety Manual 3C

*"One who goes gently goes safely, one who goes safely, goes far."*

*—Mocoa, Darién native, Colombia, 1927*

## Day 1—Classroom

**1) 08:00 Introduction and Overview—high-ranking person (i.e. Vice President, etc.)**

Objectives of overall safety program (prepare, execute, follow-up)—Why safety is the right thing to do **and** is good business

Nobody gets hurt (who, what, why)

Participant Introductions—by partner: Name, what field ops, field experience

**2) 08:30 Scenario Analysis**

*First Aid*

*Breakdown*

*Behavior*

*Group dynamics*

**3) 08:50 Why accidents occur: Intersection of Human, Environmental, and Equipment Factors** (Tied into the field activity safety system):

a) Human Factors
- i) Perceptions of risk
- ii) How people react to different situations
- iii) Abilities and Attitudes (physical abilities and condition, field experience, etc.)
- iv) Overload (planning to mitigate physical and mental fatigue)

b) Environmental Factors
- i) Overview
- ii) Cover details in next module, American Red Cross First Aid—When Help is Delayed (ARC FA-WHD)

c) Equipment Factors
- i) Overview
- ii) Cover details in next module, ARC FA-WHD

  *Quiz (to be developed by instructor)*

**09:30 BREAK**

**4) 09:45 ARC First Aid—When Help Is Delayed**

a) Types of Delayed-Help Situations: Rural, Wilderness, Disasters, Boating

b) Applying the Emergency Action Steps
- i) CHECK
  - (1) Check the scene
  - (2) Check the victim
  - (3) Check for resources
    - *(a) Exercises: Hazard ID, Patient Evaluation, Resource Requirements*
- ii) CALL
  - (1) Making a plan

## Field Activity Safety Manual 3C

(2) Getting help
(a) Calling, Improvised distress signals
(b) Sending for help, Leaving a victim alone, Transporting a victim to help (demonstrate carries, to be practiced in field on Day 2)
*(c) Exercise: group discussion and decision on how to get help*

iii) CARE
(1) Monitoring the victim
(2) Fractures and dislocations
(3) Bleeding (direct pressure, elevation, pressure points, tourniquet)
*(a) Exercise: Tourniquet application and practice*
(4) Burns
(5) Heat Exposure
(6) Sudden Illness
(7) Shock
(8) Head, Neck, and Back injuries
*(a) Exercise: In-line stabilization, log roll onto blanket*
(9) Difficult decisions

c) Protection from the weather
i) Protecting the victim
ii) Constructing shelter

d) Preparing for Emergencies
i) Types of preparation: knowledge, skills, equipment
ii) Ensuring adequate preparation: planning, risk assessment, research, scenarios
*(1) Exercise: Group brainstorm on what knowledge, skills, equipment needed for leading field schools*

e) Summary and Preview of Field Safety Process

**11:45 FA-WHD Quiz and LUNCH** *(FA-WHD Quiz)*
(American Red Cross course will supply quiz as part of their training)

**5) 13:00 Field Safety Process**
Overview of the process (Timeline from pre-trip to field execution to follow-up)
Site Summary Sheets (Review go/no go—out of bounds—etc.)
Safety Watch Role—observation—complete daily log—barriers
SWP—tie into SOP and Hazard ID
SOPs: Driving, Hiking, Special

**14:30 BREAK**

**14:45 Field Safety Process (continued)**
Tools: *Exercises— break into 4 groups and give each a pack and road kit. Rotate among 4 stations where group works through various scenarios to become familiar with gear: FA, Vehicle, Radios/Sat phone, Safety. Compare list generated during previous module with materials in kits.*

**6) 16:00 Briefing for Day 2**

**7) 16:30 Adjourn**

## Day 2—Field

**07:30 First Day Safety Briefing at office**

(model presentation using PowerPoint slides in classroom located in Section 5 of this book)

1) Introduction and General Briefing
2) Assign Drivers
3) Assign Groups or Buddy pairs and Roles
4) Brief Drivers as a sub group
5) Check everyone's required PPE (especially footwear and eye protection)
6) Issue SHE, Field stop packages, and Communications Equipment to each group
7) Identify staff roles for various stops today

**08:15 Depart for drive to field area**

Include all standard communication and in field vehicle marking protocols

*Radio check*

**FIELD STOP #1—Approach hike to panorama overlook**

We will demonstrate the roles and procedures on this stop

*Conduct site hazard analysis using Hazard Register and Site Safety Summary Sheet*

**LUNCH**

Set up who will be the staff on the next stop and their roles

**FIELD STOP #2—Cliff-top traverse to restricted-access outcrop**

Participants lead the traverse

*Site safety orientation (SWPs)*
*Hiking protocol (wandering too close to cliff)*
*Access control to narrow outcrop*
*Review new hazards identified—Fill out Field Safety Log*

**FIELD STOP #3—Short traverse to arrange class for correlation exercise in field**

Participants lead the traverse

*Arrange class into four groups for FA practice:*

*Fx forearm (SAM splint, sling, swathe)*
*Fx lower leg (anatomical splint)*
*Throw bag*
*Blanket carry*

**FIELD STOP #4—Long traverse to cliff-face exposure**

Participants lead the traverse

*Site safety orientation (SWPs)*
*Hiking protocol*
*ERP drill*

**FIELD STOP #5—Short traverse to vehicles**

Participants lead the traverse

*Head count*

*Reassemble group at vehicles*

*Head count*

*Safety debriefing: Each group fills out Safety Log for this day*

*Course Evaluations—fill out*

*Wrap up discussion*

*Briefing for return trip*

**Return to office, highway protocol**

Check in upon return to office

**Adjourn**

## A. First Aid Gear Scenarios

Using the Safety Watch Backpack, do the following:

1. You are leading a group of 19 students along a cliff-top exposure in northern California during a school in mid-October. It is the end of a long day in the field, about 5:00 p.m. You are about 2 km from the vehicles and about 90 m higher in elevation.
   While walking back to the vehicles down a steep rocky trail, one of the students trips, tumbles, and falls down the talus slope below the trail and lands about 5 m down the slope on a pile of small boulders.
   She doesn't appear to be moving and has a large cut over her right eye and blood on her right and left knees.
   Pull out and list the materials and supplies that would be used to treat this person.
2. You are near the conclusion of a 3-km hike into Tuscher Canyon on a hot, cloudless day in June, when you notice one participant stumbling near the back of the group. She appears incoherent, and her skin is hot, dry, and red. Pull out and list the materials and supplies that you would use to treat her.
3. You are about 1 km into Last Chance Canyon when a participant trips and falls into a mass of cacti by the side of the trail. Examination reveals that he has abrasions on both knees oozing blood and multiple short cactus spines (<7 mm long) in his left leg and a single spine about 2-cm long in his right leg, just under his knee Pull out and list the materials and supplies that you would use to treat him.

## B. Vehicle Safety Kit Scenarios

Using the Vehicle Safety Kit, do the following:

1. Review the flat-tire scenario presented earlier today: You are in the lead vehicle of 8 vehicles on a sinuous stretch of interstate highway in central Colorado (maps below), driving west back to the hotel at 4:30 p.m. Just after the group rounds a tight curve, the third vehicle in line suddenly pulls off to the left and stops on the left shoulder, up against the guardrail. They radio you to say that their vehicle has two flat tires in the rear, both with sidewall damage.
   Pull out and set up the equipment you would use to respond to this scenario.

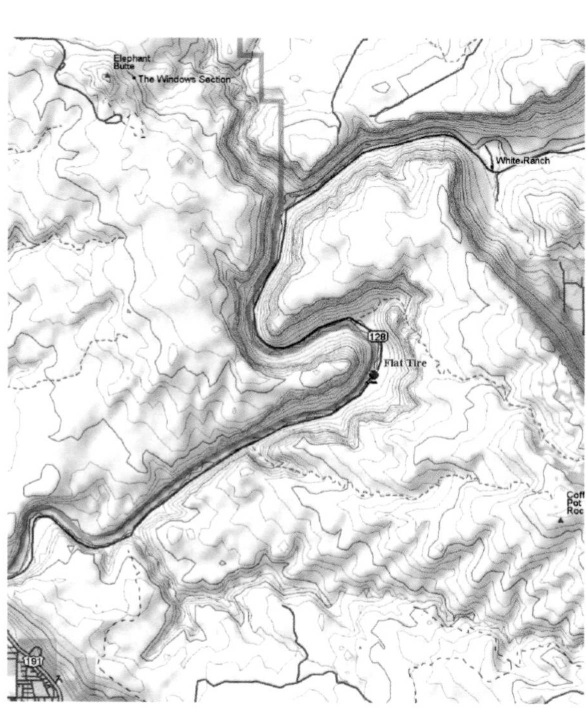


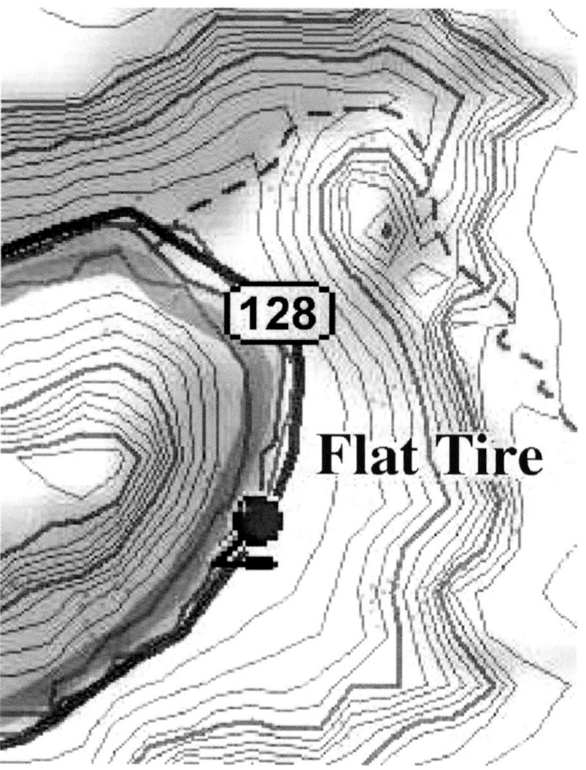

2. You return to the vehicles from an outcrop that is along a gravel road, about 10 km from the nearest paved road and about 25 km from the nearest town. You find one of the vehicles has one flat tire with sidewall damage and one rear tire that looks low. Closer examination reveals that the low-air tire has a cactus spine in the middle of the tread.
   Additionally, another vehicle has a rear tire that looks low; you cannot find any object that has punctured it, but you suspect that it lost its air from going over a particularly hard bump in the road.
   Pull out and list the equipment you would use to respond to this scenario.
3. You arrive at an outcrop that is at the end of 15 km of bad roads to discover that your vehicle's fuel tank has a small puncture about 2 mm in diameter at its lowest point that is slowly leaking gasoline. Pull out and list the equipment you would use and actions you would take to respond to this scenario.

## C. Safety Gear Scenarios

Using the Safety Watch Backpack, do the following:

1. You are leading a group of 23 students to a cliff-top exposure in order to conduct an hour-long panorama sketching exercise and discussion. There is a sheer-drop cliff edge along the front part of the outcrop and an area of loose talus and shrubbery to the rear of the area in which you wish to place the class for the exercise. Pull out and list the materials you would use to mark the out-of-bounds areas.
2. Using the lightning detector, how do you:
   Determine the battery condition?
   Determine the direction of travel of a storm?
   Silence the audible alarm and use only the visual alert?
   What can cause false readings on the lightning detector?
3. You are leading a group of 26 students through a two-hour-long outcrop exercise, examining a 500-m-long road-cut along a moderately busy state highway in central Utah (map top of next column). During the exercise it is necessary for the group to cross the road twice, at specific points in the exercise. Pull out and list the materials you would use to mark the out-of-bounds areas. What other gear and planning do you need to enhance the safety of the group during the exercise?

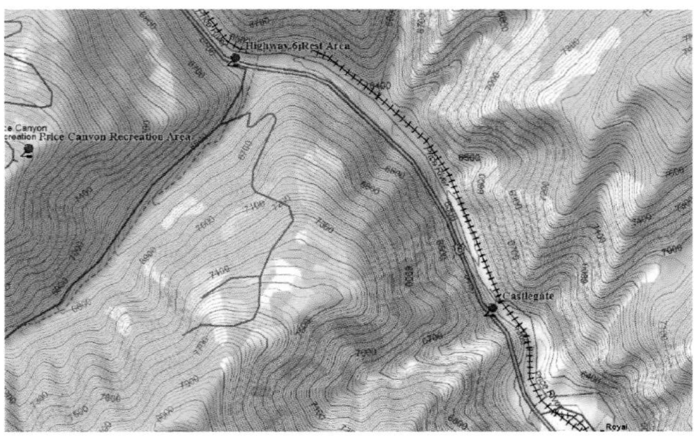


## D. Communications Gear Scenarios

1. Using the Rino radios (FRS/GPS):

   How do you turn the radio on and check the battery condition?
   How do you set the channel and CTCSS code?
   How do you turn the GPS off and leave the radio on to save the batteries?
   How do you zoom in on the GPS map?
   How do you determine your latitude and longitude?
   Which of the radios can have digital topographic maps loaded into them?
2. Using the Satellite Phone:
   How do you turn it on and check the battery condition?
   How do you turn it on and make a call?
   What factors control access to a satellite uplink?
   How do you use the regular cell phone?

## Field Safety Leadership—Initial Scenario 1

You are leading a group of 19 students along a cliff-top exposure in northern California during a school in mid-October (map and picture next page). It is the end of a long day in the field, about 5:00 p.m. You are about 2 km from the vehicles and about 90 m higher in elevation.

While walking back to the vehicles down a steep rocky trail, one of the students trips, tumbles, and falls down the talus slope below the trail and lands about 5 m down the slope on a pile of small boulders.

She doesn't appear to be moving and has a large cut over her right eye and blood on her right and left knees. What do you do?

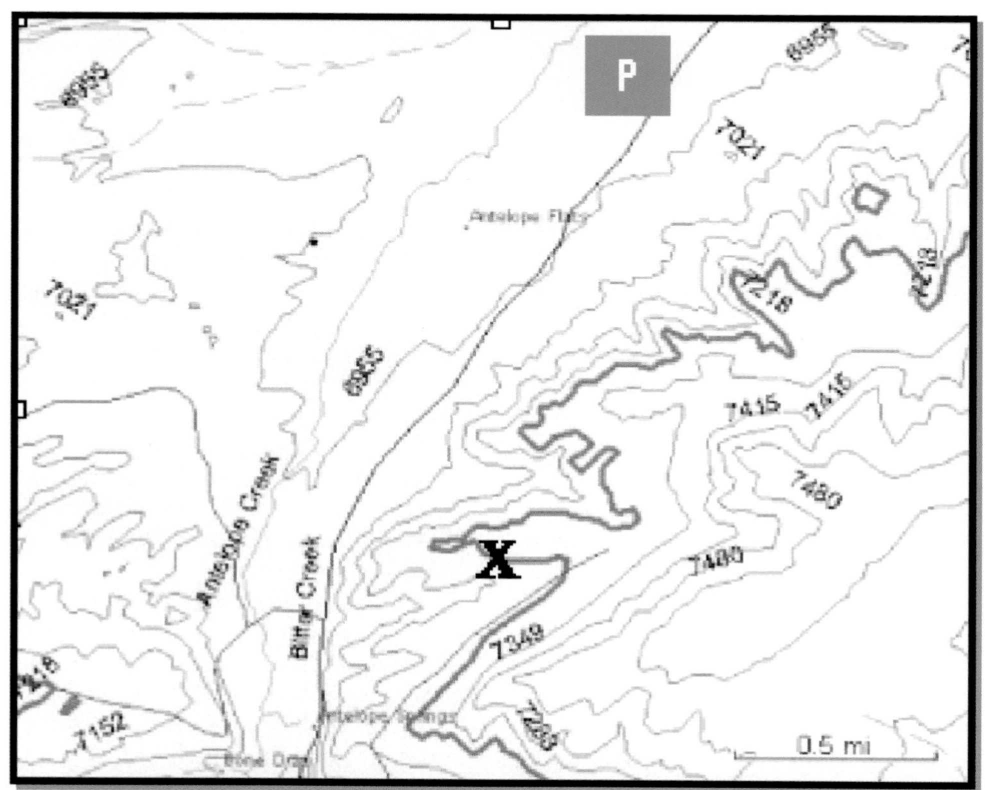
P
6955
7021
7218
7415
7480
X
7349
Antelope Creek
Bitter Creek
7152
0.5 mi

### Field Safety Leadership—Initial Scenario 2

You are in the lead vehicle of 8 vehicles on a sinuous stretch of interstate highway in central Colorado, driving west back to the hotel at 4:30 p.m.

Just after the group rounds a tight curve, the third vehicle in line suddenly pulls off to the left and stops on the left shoulder, up against the guardrail. They radio you to say that their vehicle has two flat tires in the rear. What do you do?

*[The 4 maps below show the location of the scenario at successive larger scales.]*

### Field Safety Leadership—Initial Scenario 3

You are leading a group through a series of outcrops in central Utah (picture next page). It is the third day of the field trip. One of the participants has been at the back of the group consistently during all hikes, taking pictures, often behind the Safety Watch.

You are at the top of a moderately steep slope, ready to return to the vehicles, and this same person runs about 10 m upslope off the trail, up to the edge of a 20 m cliff, knocking down numerous rocks up to 50 cm long onto the trail towards the rest of the group. What do you do?

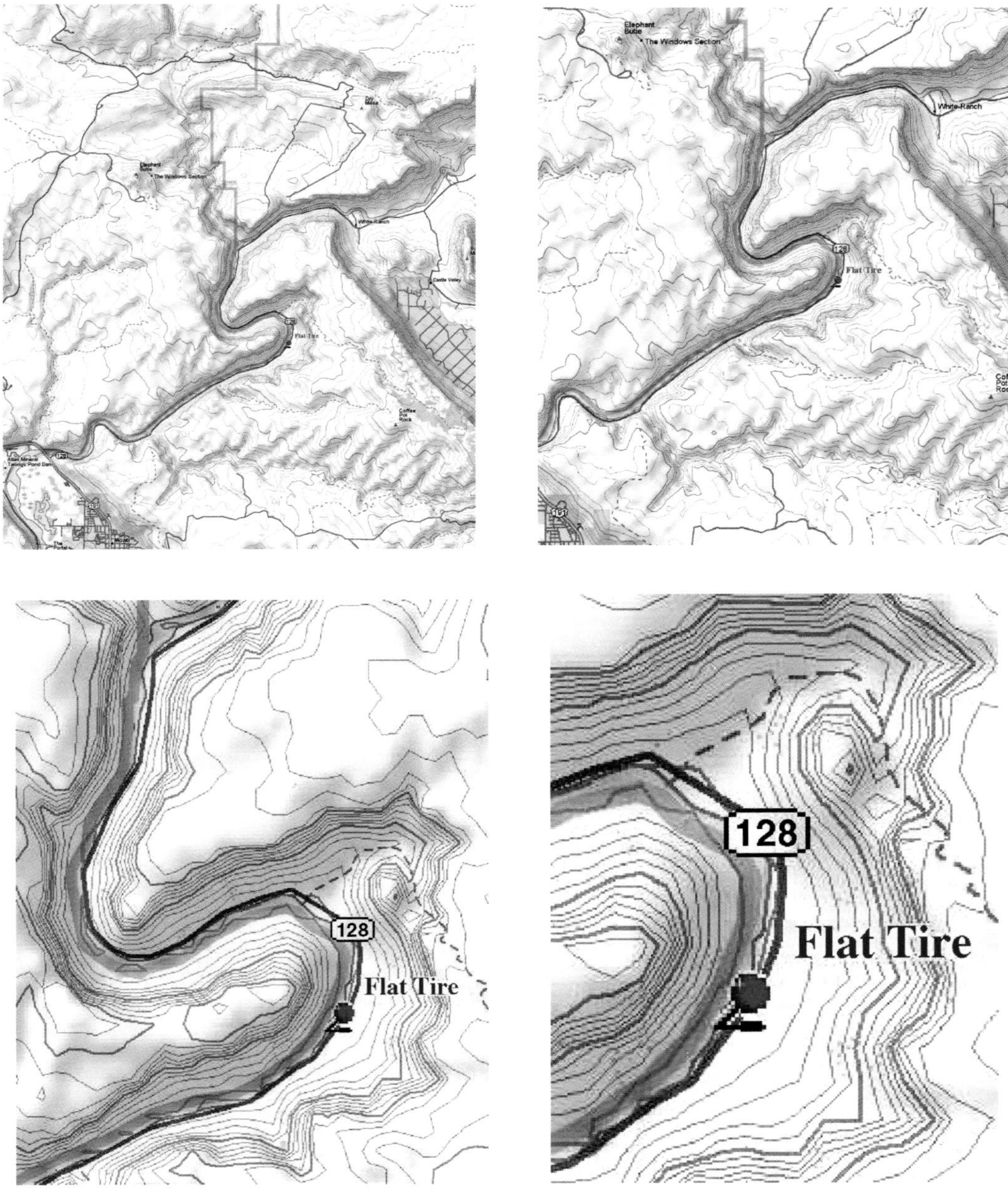

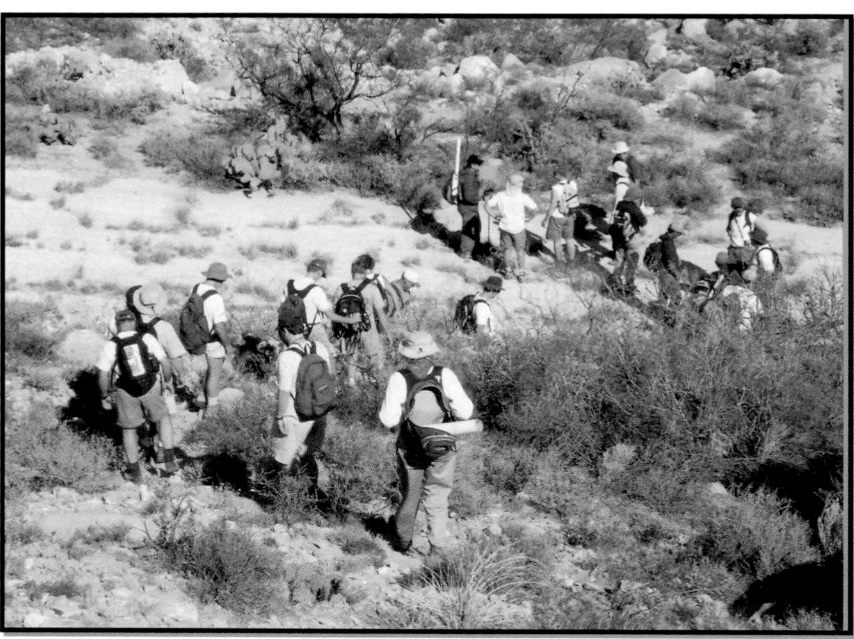

## Field Safety Leadership—Initial Scenario 4

You are leading a group of 25 in the hills of New Mexico through a series of relatively long hikes (2–3 km) to hillside scrambles up to 100 m of elevation gain (picture below).

At the conclusion of every stop, two of the participants have been racing each other back downhill to the vehicles, ahead of everyone, including the lead instructor.

In addition, four people in the group have various knee problems, and have been consistently lagging behind the group, commonly arriving back at the vehicles 10 minutes after everyone else. What do you do right now, and for the rest of the stops?

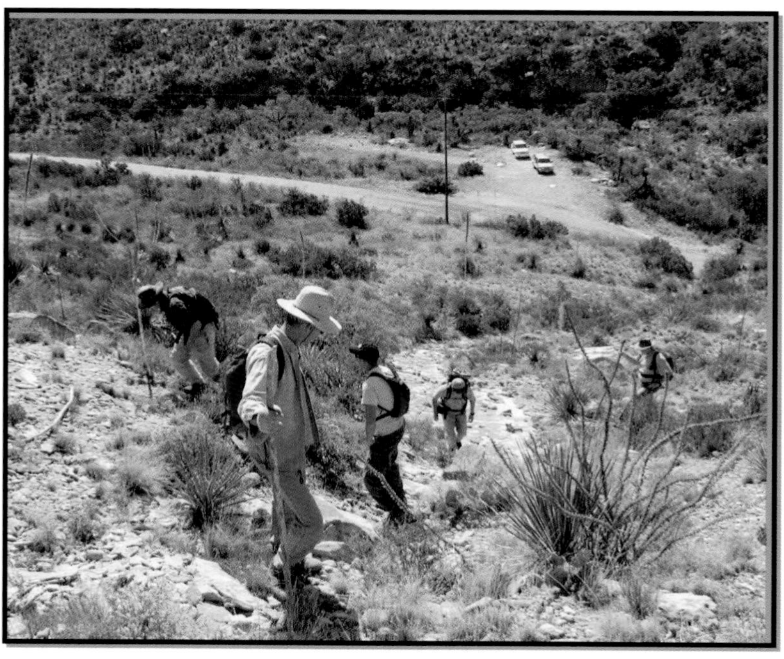

Equally important is that everyone, participants and staff, know the use and limitations of the safety gear. This includes proper choice and fitting of Personal Protective Equipment, operation of communications, navigation, and warning or barrier devices, as well as use of first aid and survival kits. Pay special attention to selecting appropriate vehicles and to choosing trained and experienced operators for them.

- Review the ***Field Activity Materials and Equipment Checklists*** and determine what items will be needed.
- Review Safety Watch pack basic contents and determine need for supplementing (form 3D, below).
- Determine the safety equipment required for the Activity and requisition from the Geoscience Field Safety Coordinator or other source (radios, satellite phones, barriers, etc.)
- Determine what Personal Protective Equipment (PPE) will be required for Participants—what they must bring and what the Activity will provide (form 3E, below). Submit preliminary requisition to the Field Safety Coordinator for Activity-supplied items.
- Determine communications needs (see form 3F, below).
- Determine vehicle needs (see forms 3G and 3H, below).

**The following forms for this section are also located on the CD-Rom accompanying this book:**
**Standard Safety Watch Pack Contents—3D**
**PPE Selection Guidelines—3E**
**Communications Equipment Guidelines—3F**
**Vehicle Selection Guidelines—3G**
**Vehicle Safety Pack Contents—3H**

## SECTION 3.4: EMERGENCY RESPONSE PLAN (ERP)–DESCRIPTION AND OUTLINE

Emergency Response Plans (ERP) describe in detail what everyone participating in the Activity does in case of an emergency. ERPs also identify what resources are available to help remedy the situation. Detailed plans save valuable time during response by determining beforehand who is to perform what functions and how. Probably the most valuable contribution of an ERP is the thought and discussions that occur while developing the plan.

### Emergency Response Plans (ERP) Should Contain the Following Information, as a Minimum

#### Copies of the ERP are Made Available to Every Participant:

- Conditions for activating ERP (injury, illness, hazardous condition)
- Actions to be taken:
  - How to activate ERP
  - Who will be in charge in case of an emergency
  - Roles and responsibilities of staff, participants, and alternates
- Emergency Resources
  - Communications
    - Equipment
      - Primary
      - Backup
    - Emergency agencies contact information
    - Translator (as needed)
      - Primary
      - Backup
  - Treatment Supplies and Equipment
- Evacuation Procedures
- Notifications to be made:
  - **Who** is to be notified:
    - Personal emergency contact—participant information in sealed envelope.
    - Organization management—refer to Organization Incident Reporting Guidelines
  - **When** notification is to be made:
    - Personal emergency contact—dependent on type and severity of incident
    - Organization management—refer to Organization Incident Reporting Guidelines
  - **How** notifications are to be made
    - Designated staff member and alternates
    - Communications mode (in person, voice, written) and equipment available
  - **What** is to be reported

The Emergency Response Plan template (form 3J, below) can be used to develop the Activity ERP.

*(text continues on page 75)*

**Satellite Phone**

**Lightning Detector**

**Field Safety Gear**

**Bull Horn**

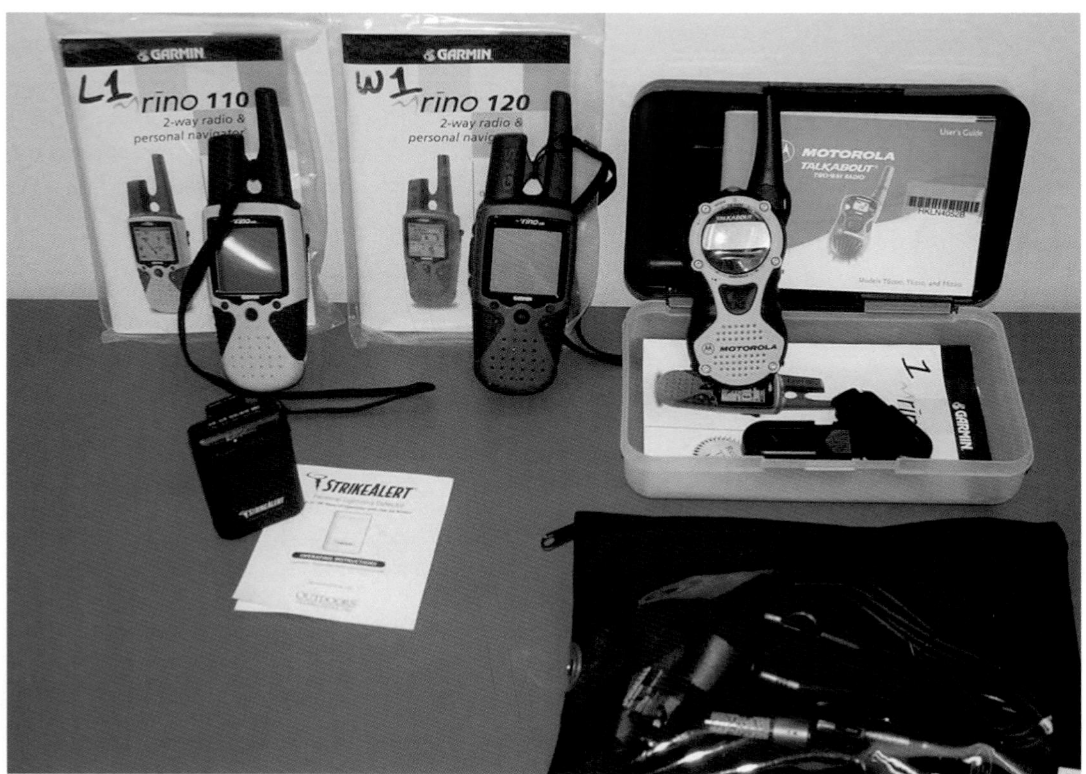


**GPS Field Radios**

**First Aid Kit**

**Safety Watch Equipment**

# Safety Watch Pack—Checklist

Kit # ___________

This checklist provides guidance for outfitting the Safety Watch pack for use on a field school or trip.

## Required Resources

- ☐ Safety Watch Backpack (Small _________) (Large __________)
- ☐ First Aid kit (How many ______)
- ☐ Flashlight
- ☐ Emergency First-Aid booklet
- ☐ Telephones: _____ Cell ___ Satellite
- ☐ Trail radio—Lead Instructor (make and model, e.g., Garmin Rino 110)
- ☐ Trail radio—Safety Watch (make and model, e.g., Motorola T6320)
- ☐ Trail radio—Logistics Coordinator (make and model, e.g., Garmin Rino 120)
- ☐ Trail radios—Assistant Instructors (make and model, e.g., Motorola T6320)
- ☐ Lightning detector
- ☐ Pin flags—for marking out of bounds
- ☐ Surveyors flagging—for marking out of bounds

- ☐ Site-specific ERP (Site Summary Sheets)—stored in plastic waterproof pouch
- ☐ ***Emergency Information and Medical Certification*** forms—stored in plastic waterproof pouch
- ☐ Safety log book

- ☐ Duct tape
- ☐ Pad, Foam (40 x 60 cm) *for First Aid treatment, splint padding, insulation, etc.*
- ☐ Space Blanket *for First Aid treatment for shock, insulation, sun shade, etc.*
- ☐ Large Trash Bag *for emergency shelter/rain gear, survival sack*
- ☐ Delegate-specific First Responder supplies
- ☐ Other (cones, warning lights):

**Issued by:** ______________________________ **Date:** ____________

**Received by:** ______________________________ **Date:** ____________

**Expected Return Date:** ____________

**Returned by:** ______________________________ **Date:** ____________

# Personal Protective Equipment Guidelines

| Activity | Required PPE | Recommended PPE |
|---|---|---|
| **Hiking**—outcrops, trails, desert environment, and loose rock. | Appropriate sturdy footwear (i.e. Hiking boots with sturdy uppers and Vibram-type non-slip soles), emergency whistle | Long pants and long sleeve shirts, sun glasses, sun screen, wide brimmed hat, water canteen, hiking stick, insect repellent, two-way communications |
| **Roadside Activities** Outcrop, road-cuts, and access to outcrops. | Safety vest (high visibility), traffic warning markers ("cones") | Traffic warning lights |
| **Sampling with rock hammers** (chipping)—outcrops, hand specimens | Safety glasses, sturdy non-slip gloves | |
| **Sampling with digging tools**—slopes, outcrops, pits ***(no deeper than knee height!)*** | Safety glasses; sturdy, non-slip gloves | Steel-toed work boots |
| **Activities in cave mouths or under overhangs** - outcrops, sampling | Hard hats, safety glasses | |
| **Boating** | PFD, Type I or II (Life vest), Footwear with non-slip soles | Sun screen, sun glasses, water canteen, wide brimmed hat, gloves if rowing, paddling, or sailing |
| **Cold weather activities**—arctic sampling, outcrops | Thermal footwear and outerwear, gloves, safety glasses, two-way communication, personal survival kit | Water proof footwear, thermal underwear, hand warmers, vehicle survival kit |
| | | |

# Communications Equipment Guidelines

### Communications Equipment Guidelines

Conducting field activities requires that two-way communication be available in the event of an emergency. Current options available include Citizen Band (CB) radios, UHF/VHF radios, cell and satellite phones. Participants on OBO activities should check with the organizer beforehand to see if two-way communications will be provided.

It is the responsibility of the Activity Coordinator to make sure that all radio equipment is properly licensed for use in the country of the activity. Permissible radio equipment and licensing requirements vary greatly among countries, and some radio equipment is forbidden in certain countries.

**CITIZEN BAND (CB) RADIOS**—CB radios are simple to use, durable, and relatively inexpensive, but have a limited range of effectiveness and the emergency frequency (channel 9) may not be monitored in remote areas. When used there should be one radio unit per vehicle. In small group situations when there is only one vehicle or parties will be splitting up to perform field work, each party should have a portable, handheld unit. Likewise, if the fieldwork involves extended hikes away from the base camp or vehicles, a portable, hand-held unit should be taken to facilitate communication.

**FAMILY RADIO SERVICE (FRS) UHF-BAND RADIOS**—Like CB radios, FRS radios are simple to use, lightweight, and inexpensive, but have a limited range of effectiveness (typically 1 km or less). They tend to be less durable than more expensive radios, but their light weight and inexpensive cost make them very handy to issue to every one in the party for short-range communications among teams. They tend to work better in open terrain, outside of vehicles. The frequencies are shared with many other people, and a "PL" or "Privacy" is desirable. They do not require a license for operation within the U.S.A.

**UHF/VHF COMMERCIAL BAND RADIOS** (e.g., Motorola)—although more expensive than the other options, commercial-band UHF/VHF radios are very rugged and dependable, some may operate over longer distances than CB radios, and broadcast in frequencies that are not crowded by the general public. Operation of UHF/VHF radios requires some training as the transmit frequencies are licensed in the U.S.A. by the FCC and must be programmed into the radio. The organization must maintain a UHF/VHF radio license.

Please note—the laws covering the usage of UHF/VHF radios in foreign countries are NOT the same as in the U.S.A. and require local licenses issued by the host government. It is advisable to obtain such radios through local contacts or the host company.

**CELL/SATELLITE PHONES**—Each Field Activity must have at least two instruments for telephone communications for emergency and business use while in the field (2 cell, 2 satellite, or 1 of each depending on coverage at field localities). Contact your organization's Communications group or the Geoscience Field Safety Coordinator for assistance. Technology and systems requirements change rapidly in the wireless telephone industry and it is essential to verify all operational information and to test all equipment before it is needed. These factors also make it advisable to lease high-end equipment rather than purchasing it.

Not all areas are covered by cellular networks and U.S.A. cell phones usually do not work outside the U.S.A. (due to systems incompatible with CDMA or TDMA). When planning a trip, investigate whether the field destination has cellular service coverage. Cell phone service providers can assist in determining coverage areas. Keep in mind that in areas of rugged terrain the transmission of cellular phone frequencies is often poor or intermittent.

Outside the U.S.A., most countries use GSM type cellphones. Once again, it is advisable to obtain such phones through local contacts or the host organization. Some models of cellular phones have "cards" (removable electronic chips) that allow the same physical phone to be used on different type systems. Verify the system in use in the destination country through local contacts or cellular service provider (commonly part of the government in many countries).

**SATELLITE PHONES**—As of early 2005, there are two (incompatible) satellite phone systems: Iridium and Globalstar. Each has their advantages and drawbacks, both in operation and cost.

## Field Activity Safety Process 3F

# Communications Equipment Guidelines

***Iridium*** telephones operate on a truly "global" system. When a call on the Iridium system is initiated, the satellite with the best signal from the portable phone establishes the connection and then "hands off" the call to as many successive satellites as necessary to route the call to the earth station (known as a Gateway) in the general area of the destination of the call. For example, a call from Madagascar to the United States wouldn't come to earth until the satellite over Arizona established the connection with the U.S.A. Gateway. At that time, the call is routed along conventional telephone landlines to the destination of the call. With Iridium, one standard rate is charged worldwide. The Iridium handset itself tends to be larger, heavier, and a bit more complicated than a Globalstar unit, but very robust.

***Globalstar***—With Globalstar, a single satellite must detect the signal from the satellite phone and also be within range of a Gateway. The call is then sent down to the Gateway, and then routed along conventional telephone landlines to the call's destination. In the previous example, using a Globalstar phone in Madagascar calling the United States, a satellite over Madagascar sends the call to the Gateway in east Africa—and then the call would be routed over traditional lines to the U.S.A. A long-distance charge is associated with calls on the Globalstar system made outside the United States and Canada, in addition to the satellite airtime. Those extra charges vary from country to country. You can find the charges for specific countries by checking Globalstar's web site at http://www.globalstarusa.com/cgi-bin/RateCalculator.cgi.

Some Globalstar phones come with a GSM telephone built in. When a call is initiated, the phone first looks for a land-based system and if unable to connect, it switches to the satellite system. Some companies also offer data service on Globalstar while in much of North America (for an additional charge, they provide a data cable and CD-Rom to allow laptop connection).

| *Type of Equipment* | | *Typical Range* | *Relative Cost* | *Advantages* | *Disadvantages* |
|---|---|---|---|---|---|
| *Radio* | | | | | |
| | FRS | 1 km | $ | Inexpensive, light weight, widely available in U.S.A., no license required | Short range, interference with other users, rel. delicate, hand held only |
| | CB | 8 km | $$ | Simple, durable, mobile and hand held, emergency channel monitored in some areas | Limited range, interference with other users and atmospheric conditions (AM) |
| | Commercial UHF/VHF | 1–8 km | $$$ | Very durable, reliable, dedicated channel, excellent range with repeaters | Relatively expensive, license required, limited range in mountainous terrain |
| *Cellular Phone* | TDMA/CDMA *(U.S.A.)* | 1 to 3 km to cell site, worldwide on system | $$ | Relatively reliable, simple operation, familiar to most users, access to worldwide system | Limited coverage in rural areas, mountainous terrain |
| | GSM *(Most other countries)* | 1 to 3 km to cell site, worldwide on system | $$ | Relatively reliable, simple operation, familiar to most users, access to worldwide system | Limited coverage in rural areas, mountainous terrain |
| *Satellite Phone* | Iridium | Worldwide | $$ to $$$ | Global coverage,* reliable | Relatively complex operation, time charges, relatively large |
| | Globalstar | Mostly worldwide | $$ to $$$ | Wide area coverage,* GSM phone option | Relatively complex operation, time charges |
| *Notes:* | | *For hand-held units. Mobile antennae can extend range significantly* | *Includes acquisition or leasing and operation* | ** Access to any satellite system requires a relatively clear and wide view of the sky, can be blocked by dense foliage or terrain. Satellite coverage varies by location and time of day.* | |

## Field Activity Safety Process 3G

# Vehicle Selection Guidelines

1. Vehicles are to be rented from a reputable company, preferably a nationally recognized organization.
2. All vehicles **must** have seatbelts for **all** passengers. Airbags and Anti-lock brakes are desired.
3. Select vehicles with higher rollover resistance ratings—some smaller SUVs are just as prone to rollovers as are 15-passenger vans (see http://www.nhtsa.dot.gov/hot/rollover/fullWebd.html). Safe operation of any SUV or 15-passenger van requires careful attention to selection of drivers, loading, and operation. The following mitigating factors can help reduce the risk of rollovers (from the U.S. Department of Transportation, NHTSA website http://www.nhtsa.dot.gov/hot/rollover/):

**What can the consumer do to reduce rollover risk?**
Since most vehicle rollovers are single-vehicle crashes, they are often preventable. They are unlike non-rollover multiple-vehicle crashes involving frontal, side and rear impacts, where another driver may have been responsible for the crash. To minimize the risk of a rollover crash and serious injury, the driver should:

- **Always Wear Seat Belts**
  Regardless of vehicle choice, the consumer and his or her passengers can dramatically reduce their risk of being killed or seriously injured in a rollover crash by simply using their seat belts. Seat belt use has an even greater effect on reducing the deadliness of rollover crashes than on other crashes because so many victims of rollover crashes die as a result of being partially or completely thrown from the vehicle. NHTSA estimates that belted occupants are about 75% less likely to be killed in a rollover crash than unbelted occupants.
- **Avoid Conditions That Lead to Loss of Control**
  Common reasons drivers lose control of their vehicles and run off of the road include: driving under the influence of alcohol or drugs, driving while sleepy or inattentive, or driving too fast for the conditions.
- **Be Careful on Rural Roads**
  Drivers should be particularly cautious on curved rural roads and maintain a safe speed to avoid running off the road and striking a ditch or embankment and rolling over.
- **Avoid Extreme Panic-like Steering**
  Another condition that may cause a rollover is where a driver overcorrects the steering as a panic reaction to an emergency or to something as simple as dropping a wheel off the pavement. Especially at freeway speeds, over correcting or excessive steering may cause the driver to lose control resulting in the vehicle sliding sideways and rolling over. If your vehicle should go off the roadway, gradually reduce the vehicle speed and then ease the vehicle back on to the roadway when it is safe to do so.
- **Maintain Tires Properly**
  Since maintaining vehicle control is the most important factor in minimizing the chances of a vehicle rollover, improperly inflated and worn tires can be dangerous. Worn tires may cause the vehicle to slide sideways on wet or slippery pavement, resulting in the vehicle sliding off the road and increasing the risk of rolling over. Improper inflation can accelerate tire wear, and can even lead to catastrophic failures. It is important that consumers maintain tires properly and replace them, when necessary.
- **Load Vehicles Properly**
  Consult your owner's manual to determine the maximum safe load for your vehicle, and the proper distribution of that load. Pay special attention to the vehicle manufacturer's instructions and weight limits when using any type of roof rack. Any load placed on the roof will be above the center of gravity of the vehicle and will increase the likelihood of rolling over.

4. Select vehicles appropriate to local conditions, paying special attention to ground clearance, passenger and cargo capacity, type of tires, engine power, and availability of full-size spare tires. Check all these attributes when taking delivery of vehicles. All vehicles must have functioning seatbelts for all passengers.
5. Consult workers with experience in the locations to be visited when selecting vehicles.
6. All vehicles for use on unpaved roads must have at least one full-size spare tire and two full-size spares per vehicle are strongly recommended. If possible, hire the same type of vehicle to allow sharing of spare tires between vehicles.

## Field Activity Safety Process 3H

# Emergency Highway Kit—Checklist

Kit #__________

This checklist is to provide assistance outfitting the Emergency Highway Kit for use on a field school or trip.

### Required Resources

- ❑ Carry Bag
- ❑ Jumper Cables
- ❑ Tow Rope
- ❑ 12 v light
- ❑ Tools
  - pliers
    - 7.5 in. diagonal
    - 6.5 in. long nose locking
    - 8 in. slip joint
    - 10 in. pump
  - screw drivers
    - 3/16 in. slotted
    - ¼ in slotted
    - #1 Philips
    - #2 Philips
    - 4-in-1 pocket
  - hex wrenches
- ❑ Gloves
  - two pair latex
  - two pair grip
- ❑ Tire Gauge
- ❑ Safety Glasses (two pair)
- ❑ Strobe Light (**2 D batteries**)
- ❑ Bungee Cord
  - two 24 in.
  - two 36 in.
- ❑ 12 v tire pump
  - two bottles Slime
- ❑ Reflective Safety Vests (2)
- ❑ Folding shovel
- ❑ Siphon/Pump
- ❑ Large Plastic Bag
- ❑ Tape
  - duct
  - electrical
- ❑ Space Blanket
- ❑ Super Glue
- ❑ Gas Tank Sealant
- ❑ Sheet metal Screws w/ rubber and metal washers
- ❑ Kwick Kones w/ 2 strobe lights (**each light requires 4 AA batteries**)

---

**Issued by:**____________________________________ **Date:**__________

**Received by:**____________________________________ **Date:**__________

**Name of Trip:** ____________________________________________

**School or Trip Job Number:**______________ **Expected Return Date:**__________

**Returned by:**____________________________________ **Date:**__________

*"The worst thing you can do is to get frightened. The truly dangerous enemy is not the cold or the hunger, so much as the fear. It robs the wanderer of his judgment and of his limb power, it is fear that turns the passing experience into a final tragedy. . .Keep cool and all will be well. . .Use what you have, where you are, right now."*

*Ernest Thompson Seton, 1906*

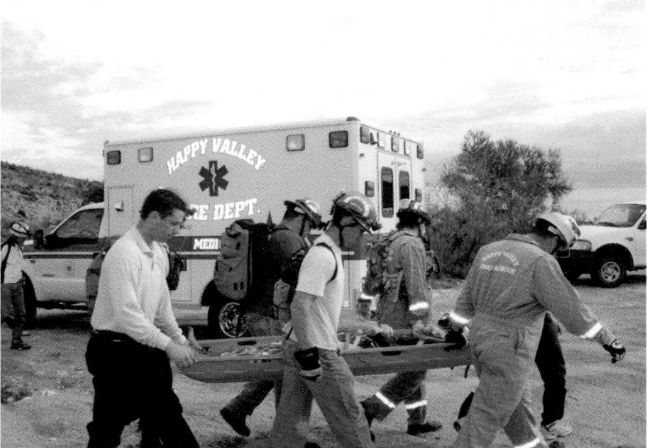

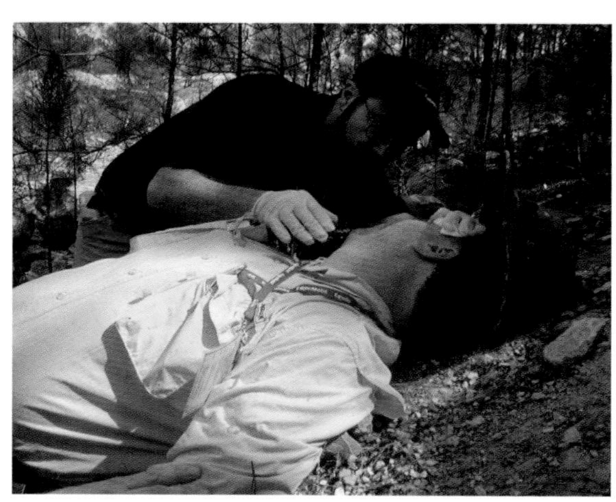

## Emergency Response Plan

### For Field Schools and Field Trips

Most of the detailed ERP information is captured on Site Safety Summary sheets, which capture data on normal and emergency operations at a specific field site including: specific location of and directions to the site and emergency resources, parking and normal operations areas, No Go criteria, accessibility, emergency contact information, safe work practices, and safety briefing highlights (see form 3K, below). The overall ERP for Schools and Trips is captured in the Standard ERP Roles and Responsibilities (see form 3I, below). A summary of the key points of the ERP, including Standard Roles and Responsibilities, is issued to each participant on a pocket-sized card (see form 5C, in Section 5).

### For Activities in Foreign Countries

The ERP must be coordinated with the local branch of the home organization or a local organization or contact in that country. In most cases, the Activity ERP will consist of "on-site" response actions by the Activity staff with reporting, notification, and evacuation requirements determined by the local organization's existing ERP. An appropriate level "bridging document" defining the relationship and connection of the Activity ERP and local organization's ERP will need to be developed by the Activity Staff and approved by the management of both organizations. The local organization ERP becomes a part of the Activity ERP. An appropriate number of translators must be determined and people identified to handle this duty.

Discussions should be held with the local SHE representative as early as possible in the planning process to ensure that all issues are identified and appropriately addressed. The Geoscience Field Safety Coordinator will assist in this process.

**The following forms for this section are also located on the CD-Rom accompanying this book:**
**ERP Standard Roles and Responsibilities—3I**
**Emergency Response Plan (blank form)—3J**
**Site Safety Summary Sheet (blank form)—3K**

## SECTION 3.5: COMMUNICATIONS WITH PARTICIPANTS

This section outlines the flow of information between the Activity Coordinator and participants in chronological order. A package with specific information about the Activity, including its technical and SHE components as well as logistical and other details, is prepared by the Activity Staff. The package is reviewed by the Activity Coordinator and made available to the Activity Owner for review. This information is then sent to each participant along with two standard forms that request basic personal data and acknowledgement of understanding of the safety issues. The participant must return the forms, acknowledging the receipt of safety information and providing personal information that can then be used to modify course delivery and provide emergency assistance. The Activity Coordinator reviews all responses and the Activity Staff uses the aggregate data to fine-tune their preparations for conducting that particular session.

## Pre-Activity Package

The Activity Coordinator and Staff are responsible for assembling the Pre-Activity Package to send to Participants. The Package includes the following 5 documents:

- **Pre-Activity Management Letter:**
  - A cover letter designed to highlight the importance of safe operations through a direct communication from a high-level person (manager, chairperson, executive) in the home organization. Contains greetings, reinforcement on the core value of safety, consequences of unsafe activities, and possible disciplinary actions for reckless behavior.
  - Must be modified for the specific instance of the Field Activity being planned and signed by the appropriate management representative. A generic letter is attached (form 3L, below).

> NOTE: The red italicized parts of the Management Letter are to be replaced with Activity-specific names, dates, etc.

  - To be kept by participant for reference in Activity preparation and participation.
- **Pre-Activity Safety Assessment:**
  - Contains a Technical and Logistical Overview, Basic Safety Considerations, Basic Physical/Health requirements. Includes a detailed description of typical activities with an emphasis on the most physically demanding.
    - Summary of common hazards with prevention/mitigation measures
    - Description of activity-specific personal protective equipment

*(text continued on page 86)*

# Emergency Response Plan (ERP) Standard Responsibilities
## Field School/Trip

**Group with injured/ill member:**

- Activates ERP with voice, whistle, radio, etc.
- Remain with/near injured, if safe to do so
- Prevent further harm—DO NOT MOVE injured/ill person
- Identify urgent issues: level of consciousness, breathing, pulse, severe bleeding

**Uninvolved groups:**

- Congregate around assistant instructor, if safe to do so
- If not safe to congregate, remain in place
- Await instructions

**Assistant Instructor (middle of the pack):**

- Assembles uninvolved groups in a safe place
- Conducts head count
- Stands by to assist, as needed
- Leads alternative activity or evacuation of uninvolved groups as required

**Safety Watch:**

- Acknowledges activation of ERP
- Proceeds to location of injured
- Provides initial First Aid
- Assesses additional needs
- Requests additional resources as needed

**Logistics Coordinator:**

- Assists Assistant Instructor with uninvolved groups
- Assists with emergency notification and evacuation

**Lead Instructor:**

- Acknowledges activation of ERP
- Determines severity of situation
- Decides on course of action for patient and uninvolved groups
- Communicates plan to all and checks for understanding and compliance
- Coordinates treatment, notification, and evacuation

***Alternative Situations and Roles:***

**Lead Instructor injured or ill**

- Assistant Instructor substitutes for Lead Instructor
- Designated participant substitutes for Assistant Instructor

**Assistant Instructor injured or ill:**

- Designated participant substitutes for Assistant Instructor

**Safety Watch injured or ill:**

- Assistant Instructor substitutes for Safety Watch
- Designated participant substitutes for Assistant Instructor

## Field Activity Safety Process 3J

# Emergency Response Plan

**Activity:** ______________________ **Dates:** ____________

**Activate in case of:**

| | |
|---|---|
| | Illness |
| | Injury |
| | Hazardous Condition |
| | *Other?* |

**How to Activate:** Notify others in the field by:

| | |
|---|---|
| | Voice |
| | Whistle |
| | Radio |
| | *Other?* |

**Initial Emergency Action Steps:**

1. **Approach injured/ill person safely**
2. **Prevent further harm–DO NOT MOVE injured**
3. **Identify urgent issues: unconsciousness, breathing, pulse, severe bleeding**

| Roles: | Primary | Alternate: |
|---|---|---|
| In **Charge overall** | ***Activity Coordinator (AC)*** | *Assistant Instructor* |
| **Check** the patient | ***Safety Watch (SW)*** | *Assistant Instructor* |
| **Call** for assistance | ***Safety Watch (SW)*** | *Assistant Instructor* |
| Provide **Care** | ***Safety Watch (SW)*** | *Assistant Instructor* |
| Take charge of uninvolved persons | ***Assistant Instructor (AI)*** | *Selected participant* |
| **Assist** with care | ***Selected participant (SP)*** | *Selected participant* |
| Provides peripheral support | ***Logistics Coordinator (LC)*** | *Selected participant* |

**Emergency Plan:**

| *Condition:* | *Actions:* | *Follow-up:* |
|---|---|---|
| **If Accident Occurs:** | - Stop and Check for Injuries/Illness<br>- Provide First Aid care as needed | > Record details in Safety Log |
| **If NO Further Care Required:** | | |
| | - Proceed with planned activities<br>- Check with medical services in town upon return *(interface with local ERP/organization medical resources?)* | Property Damage only:<br>-Notify Supervisor<br>-File Report upon return to office<br>> Notify Supervisor in case of injury<br>> File appropriate report<br>***(Consult your Organization Guidelines)*** |
| **If Further Care IS Required:** | | |
| **If Patient IS ABLE to evacuate under own power or with help** | **SW** assists patient out and drives to medical facility<br>**AI** takes charge of remaining group<br>**AC** and Staff initiate Change Management process to determine actions and communicate to remaining group<br>***(Activate Alternate Roles using pre-selected Participant)*** | > Notify Supervisor as soon as practical<br>> File appropriate report<br>***(Consult your Organization Guidelines)*** |
| **If Patient needs Emergency Evacuation:** | - Contact EMS (First Responders) via telephone or radio *(interface with local ERP?)*<br>**SW**—stabilize patient, monitor vitals, provide TLC<br>- Send **LC** to meet First Responders<br>- **AI** takes charge of remaining group<br>- Patient's group assists with evacuation<br>- **SW** will accompany or follow patient to hospital<br>***(Activate Alternate Roles using pre-selected Participant)*** | > Notify Supervisor as soon as practical<br>> File appropriate report<br>***(Consult your Organization Guidelines)*** |

## Field Activity Safety Process 3J

# Emergency Response Plan

**Communications Equipment**

| Type | Phone Number/Frequency: |
|---|---|
| Cell Phone | |
| Satellite Phone | |
| Radio | |

**Emergency Contacts (EMS, Fire, Law, Search and Rescue, Hospitals with Emergency Depts.):**

| Dates/Area | Agency, Location | Phone Number |
|---|---|---|
| | *(or "See attached Site Summary Sheets")* | **nnn-nnn-nnnn** |
| | | **nnn-nnn-nnnn** |
| | | |

**Evacuation:**

| Appropriate Response | Resources: |
|---|---|
| Evacuate under own power or w/ assistance | *There are there sufficiently strong participants to assist?* |
| Pick up with wheeled vehicle | *There is access to incident site with rent truck?* |
| Needs litter evacuation | *Emergency First Responders are?* |
| Needs technical rescue | *Search and Rescue group is?* |
| Needs helicopter airlift | *How to access? Limitations: areas, times, weather?* |

**Notifications:**

| Situation: | Appropriate Response | Time Frame: |
|---|---|---|
| **Property Damage only** | Notify Supervisor verbally<br>Submit form? to Risk Management and SHE | As soon as possible<br>Within 5 working |
| **Minor Injury/Illness** | Notify Supervisor verbally | As soon as possible |
| **Serious Injury/Illness** | Notify Supervisor verbally | As soon as possible |
| **Fatality** | Notify Supervisor verbally | As soon as possible |
| **Environmental Damage** | Notify Supervisor verbally | As soon as possible |

Consult your Organization Guidelines.

**What to report:**

| | |
|---|---|
| **Who** is involved? | **When** did it happen? (date, time) |
| **What** is the nature of the illness or injury? | **Where** is (are) the involved person(s)? |
| **What** is being done? | **How** did it happen? (nature of activity) |

**Activity:** ______________________ **Dates:** ____________

***Emergency Contacts—Activity Staff***

| Staff Member | Contact Name | Contact Number(s) | | |
|---|---|---|---|---|
| | | Home | Work | Cellular/ Pager (p) |
| | | | | |
| | | | | |
| | | | | |

***Office Contacts*** *(Add to and/or modify as appropriate)*

| Description | Name | Telephone Numbers | | |
|---|---|---|---|---|
| | | Work | Home | Cell |
| Supervisor | | | | |
| Manager | | | | |
| Vice President | | | | |
| SHE Contact | | | | |

***Organization Medical Contacts*** *(Add to and/or modify as appropriate)*

| Description | Name | Telephone Numbers |
|---|---|---|
| After-hours nurse? | | |
| Medical provider? | | |

## Field Activity Safety Process

# EMERGENCY RESPONSE PLAN

**Activity:** FSL School to Blue Lagoon **Dates:** 3-19-05

**Activate in case of:**

| | |
|---|---|
| x | Illness |
| x | Injury |
| x | Hazardous Condition |
| | *Other?* |

**How to Activate:** Notify others in the field by:

| | |
|---|---|
| x | Voice |
| x | Whistle |
| | Radio |
| | *Other?* |

**Initial Emergency Action Steps:**

1. **Approach injured/ill person safely**
2. **Prevent further harm—DO NOT MOVE injured**
3. **Identify urgent issues: unconsciousness, breathing, pulse, severe bleeding**

| Roles: | Primary: | Alternate: |
|---|---|---|
| In **Charge overall** | John Smith (AC) | Bill Green (AI) |
| **Check** the patient | Jane Black (SW) | (AC) |
| **Call** for assistance | (AC) | (AI) |
| Provide **Care** | (SW) | (AC) |
| Take charge of uninvolved persons | (AI) | (SP) |
| **Assist** with care | (AI) | (SP) |
| Provides peripheral support | Jeff Hartley (LC) | (SP) |
| AC = Activity Coordinator,<br>AI = Assistant Instructor<br>SW = Safety Watch | SP = Selected participant<br>LC = Logistics Coordinator | |

**Emergency Plan:**

| *Condition:* | *Actions:* | *Follow-up:* |
|---|---|---|
| **If Accident Occurs:** | - Stop and Check for Injuries/Illness<br>- Provide First Aid care as needed | > Record details in Safety Log |
| **If NO Further Care Required:** | | |
| | - Proceed with planned activities<br>- Check with medical services in town upon return *(interface with local ERP/ organization medical resources?)* | Property Damage only:<br>- Notify Manger<br>- File Report upon return to office<br>> Notify Manger in case of injury<br>> File appropriate report<br>***(Consult your Organization Guidelines)*** |
| **If Further Care IS Required:** | | |
| **If Patient IS ABLE to evacuate under own power or with help** | **SW** assists patient out and drives to medical facility<br>**AI** takes charge of remaining group<br>**AC** and Staff initiate Change Management process to determine actions and communicate to remaining group<br>***(Activate Alternate Roles using pre-selected Participant)*** | > Notify Manager as soon as practical<br>> File appropriate report<br>***(Consult your Organization Guidelines)*** |
| **If Patient needs Emergency Evacuation:** | - Contact EMS (First Responders) via telephone or radio *(interface with local ERP??)*<br>**SW**—Stabilize patient, monitor vitals, provide TLC<br>- Send **LC** to meet First Responders<br>- **AI** takes charge of remaining group<br>- Patient's group assists with evacuation<br>- **SW** will accompany or follow patient to hospital<br>***(Activate Alternate Roles using pre-selected Participant)*** | > Notify Manager as soon as practical<br>> File appropriate report<br>***(Consult your Organization Guidelines)*** |

Field Activity Safety Process

# EMERGENCY RESPONSE PLAN

**Activity:** FSL School to Blue Lagoon **Dates:** 3-19-05

**Communications Equipment**

| Type | Phone Number/Frequency: |
|---|---|
| Cell Phone | 123-456-7890 John Smith (Primary)<br>123-456-7890 Jane Black (Backup) |
| Satellite Phone | Not Applicable |

**Emergency Contacts (EMS, Fire, Law, Search and Rescue, Hospitals with Emergency Departments):**

| Dates/Area | Agency, Location | Phone Number |
|---|---|---|
| 1/11/05 | EMS | 911 |
| 1/11/05 | Pleasantville Memorial Hospital, I45, exit 114 | 123-456-7890 |

**Evacuation:**

| Appropriate Response: | Resources: |
|---|---|
| Evacuate under own power or w/ assistance | *There are there sufficiently strong participants to assist* |
| Pick up with wheeled vehicle | *There is access to incident site with rent truck?* |
| Needs litter evacuation | *Emergency First Responders are?* |
| Needs technical rescue | *Search and Rescue group is?* |
| Needs helicopter airlift | *How to access? Limitations: areas, times, weather?* |

**Notifications:**

| Situation: | Appropriate Response: | Time Frame: |
|---|---|---|
| **Property Damage only** | Notify Manger verbally | As soon as possible |
| | | Within 5 working days |
| **Minor Injury/Illness** | Notify Manger verbally | As soon as possible |
| **Serious Injury/Illness** | Notify Manger verbally | As soon as possible |
| **Fatality** | Notify Manger verbally | As soon as possible |
| **Environmental Damage** | Notify Manger verbally | As soon as possible |

**What to report:**

| | |
|---|---|
| **Who** is involved? | **When** did it happen? (date, time) |
| **What** is the nature of the illness or injury? | **Where** is (are) the involved person(s)? |
| **What** is being done? | **How** did it happen? (nature of activity) |

***Emergency Contacts—Activity Staff***

| Staff Member | Contact Name | Contact Number(s) | | |
|---|---|---|---|---|
| | | Home | Work | Cellular/Pager (p) |
| John Smith | XXX | 123-456-7890 | 123-456-7890 | 123-456-7890 |
| Jane Black | XXX | 123-456-7890 | 123-456-7890 | 123-456-7890 |
| Bill Green | XXX | 123-456-7890 | 123-456-7890 | 123-456-7890 |

**Office Contacts** (Add to and/or modify as appropriate)

| Description | Name | Telephone Numbers | | |
|---|---|---|---|---|
| | | Work | Home | Cell |
| Manager | Mr. Manager | 123-456-7890 | 123-456-7890 | 123-456-7890 |
| Vice President | Mrs. Vice President | 123-456-7890 | 123-456-7890 | 123-456-7890 |
| SHE Contact | Mrs. SHE Contact | 123-456-7890 | 123-456-7890 | 123-456-7890 |
| Admin | Mr. Admin | 123-456-7890 | 123-456-7890 | 123-456-7890 |

**Organization Medical Contacts** (Add to and/or modify as appropriate)

| Description | Name | Telephone Numbers |
|---|---|---|
| Organization After-hours nurse | Mr. After-hours | 123-456-7890 |
| Organization Nurse Practitioner | Ms. Nurse Practitioner | 123-456-7890 |

Field Activity Safety Process 3K

# Site Safety Summary

**Field Stop Designation:** *Short descriptive name of locality, e.g., Gentile Wash, Antelope Creek*

**Field Stop Category:** *Type, length, and intensity of activity at site: hiking, climbing, swimming, etc.*

**Created for (Author):** *Name of School/Trip and Who created it*
**Activity used for:** *Name of School/Trip and Who is coordinator*
*Date of last revision* *Mo-day-yr*

**General Site Information** *Elevation—Feet or Meters*

| Geographic Location: | Latitude: | **From GPS/Map** | Longitude: | **From GPS/Map** |
|---|---|---|---|---|
| Nearest EMS: | *Contact information for nearest emergency medical services first responders. Prefer a full telephone number (10-digits in U.S.A.) to 911.*<br>*Check with local sheriff's office to see that 911 is actually implemented in the area.*<br>*Check to see where 911 calls from cellular phones are answered in a particular area—in some states all 911 cell phone calls are answered at one central location which may be very far away from the field site. In some localities, the best first contact may be with the state police, highway patrol, or county sheriff's office.* | | | |
| Backup EMS: | *Contact information for backup emergency medical services first responders. May be the state police, highway patrol, or county sheriff's office. Prefer a full telephone number (10-digits in U.S.A.) to 911.* | | | |
| Nearest ED: | *Contact information and driving directions from the site to the nearest provider of emergency medical care. It may be a hospital with an Emergency Department (ED), a clinic, or other provider. Check that the local hospital has an ED that is continuously staffed.* | | | |
| Go/No Go Criteria: | **NO GO:** *What are the conditions under which approach to or activities at the site should be curtailed or canceled? May include "Heavy rains during past 2 days" if access is on dirt roads that have swelling clay soils. Typical criteria are "Electrical storms," Heavy Rains or Snow, "Within 2 hours of high tide," or "Wave heights over 1 m." Note also possibility of flash floods in canyons if rain falls upstream. Consider lighting conditions on outcrop faces and light available for drive out from outcrop at end of activity, e.g., "must plan for one-hour of daylight for exit drive."* | | | |
| Directions to site | *Driving directions to the site from a nearby generally recognizable landmark (typically an exit from a major highway or major road junction). Used to guide emergency assistance to the site and for inexperienced instructors during normal operations.* | | | |
| Parking Areas: | **Primary**—*Description/directions to main site where all vehicles can be parked safely. Consider how changing weather conditions may impede access to the vehicles from the outcrop or egress from the site.* | | | |
| | **Secondary**—*Description/directions to backup site where all vehicles can be parked safely. Used in case primary site is already occupied by vehicles or is otherwise unsuitable.* | | | |
| Assembly Areas: | **Primary**—*Description/directions to first-choice area where all participants can assemble safely for technical introduction to site and site safety briefing.* | | | |
| | **Secondary**—*Description/directions to backup area where all participants can assemble safely. Used in case primary site is already occupied or is otherwise unsuitable.* | | | |
| Personal Protective Equipment (PPE) | **Required**—Such as boots, safety glasses, PFDs, hardhats, etc.<br>**Recommended**—Walking sticks, gloves, long pants, etc. | | | |
| Out of Bounds Areas | *Verbal description of area marked on map on reverse side of this form, indicating the reasons why or when the areas are out of bounds. Include specific directions for use of barriers, markers, etc.)* | | | |
| Cell phone coverage | *Good/spotty/none. Note nearest location with good coverage.* | Sattelite phone coverage | *Good/spotty/none. Note nearest location with good coverage.* | |
| Restroom Facilities: | *Are restroom facilities available at or near the site? If not, where are the nearest restrooms along the route, to assist with planning the day's activities.* | | | |
| Wheelchair Access: | *Easy/Difficult/Practically Impossible/Unsafe. Note alternative locations/routes/areas where wheelchair-bound attendee could participate to some degree if not reasonably able to access entire route of the class. Level of access should be assessed at time of original risk assessment, to provide an objective evaluation of the extent of wheelchair access and whether reasonable accommodations can be made that allow safe participation.* | | | |

## Safe Work Practices

- *Note key prevention and mitigation factors, equipment, and behaviors highlighted on Standard Hazard Register for the site. Enter up to 6 key points to make during short site safety briefing. See example Site Summary Sheet (in the Emergency Response Plan in this Section) for typical points.*
- 
- 
- 
- 

Field Activity Safety Process **3K**

# Site Safety Summary

| | | | |
|---|---|---|---|
| **Field Stop Designation**: | *Short descriptive name of locality, e.g., Gentile Wash, Antelope Creek* | | |
| **Field Stop Category:** | *Type, length, and intensity of activity at site: hiking, climbing, swimming, etc.* | | |
| **Created for (Author):**<br>**Activity used for:** | *Name of School/Trip and Who created it*<br>*Name of School/Trip and Who is coordinator* | *Date of last revision* | *Mo-day-yr* |

***Insert Maps of approach route and detailed outcrop traverse routes, representative photographs of general terrain and areas requiring extra caution, etc. here.***

Field Activity Safety Process 3K

# Site Safety Summary

**Field Stop Designation:** **Stop Name**

**Field Stop Category:** **Type of stop**

**Created for (Author):** **Activity name** (Author)
**Activity used for:** **Activity name** (Author)

Date of last revision: X-X-XX Initials

## General Site Information *Elevation*

| Geographic Location: | Latitude: | XX° X.X | Longitude: | XX° X.X |
|---|---|---|---|---|
| Nearest EMS: | | | | |
| Backup EMS: | | | | |
| Nearest ED: | | | | |
| Go/No Go Criteria: | NO GO: XXXXXXXXX | | | |
| Directions to site | | | | |
| Parking Areas: | Primary— | | | |
| | Secondary— | | | |
| Assembly Areas: | Primary— | | | |
| | Secondary— | | | |
| Personal Protective Equipment (PPE) | Required<br>Recommended | | | |
| Out of Bounds Areas | | | | |
| Cell phone coverage | | Satellite phone coverage | | |
| Restroom Facilities: | | | | |
| Wheelchair Access: | | | | |

## Safe Work Practices

- 
- 
- 
- 
- 

**Field Stop Designation:** **Stop Name**

**Field Stop Category:** **Type of stop**

**Created for (Author):** **Activity name** (Author)
**Activity used for:** **Activity name** (Author)

Date of last revision: X-X-XX Initials

# Field Activity Safety Process

## Site Safety Summary

**Field Stop Designation:** **Pleasantville Canyon Traverse and Overview**

**Field Stop Category:** **Hike along abandoned road and off trail ascent/descent**

**Created for (Author):** **Brushy School 03 (J. Smith and J. Black)** **Date of last revision:** **2-7-05 SRO**

**Activity used for:** **Brushy School 05 (B. Green)**

**General Site Information** *Elevation*

| | | | | |
|---|---|---|---|---|
| Geographic Location: | Latitude: | 11° 11.111'N | Longitude: | 11° 11.111' W |
| Nearest EMS: | Pleasantville National Park **123-456-7890** | | | |
| Backup EMS: | Pleasantville Fire Dept. **123-456-7890** | | | |
| Nearest ED: | Pleasantville Medical Center, Pleasantville, AA, 2430 West Street, **123-456-7890** (on far north side of town, past mall—proceed north on South Street (main road in town), becomes West Street after bend at north side of town). | | | |
| Go/No Go Criteria: | **Heavy rain, strong wind, electrical storms** | | | |
| Directions to site | ***West on Hwy. 180 from National Park Headquarters to highway dept. storage lot at intersection of new and old road (south side)*** | | | |
| Parking Areas: | Primary—South side of highway across from Pleasantville trail head | | | |
| | Secondary—NA | | | |
| Assembly Areas: | Primary—At Lead Vehicle | | | |
| | Secondary—NA | | | |
| Personal Protective Equipment (PPE) | Required—Boots and Water/Sports Drink<br>Recommended—Hat and Sunscreen and Walking Sticks | | | |
| Out of Bounds Areas | **Pavement of highway**<br>**Drop and cliff areas along hike—Do not stray from group** | | | |
| Cell phone coverage | **Yes** | Sat phone coverage | **Yes** | |
| Restroom Facilities: | **None—Use bushes or topography** | | | |
| Wheelchair Access: | **No—Long rugged hike—(yes at Overview parking area)** | | | |

**Safe Work Practices**

- Hiking off trail procedures (key positioning of SW to see all participants)
- Split group SOP—including 2 First Aid kits required for Stop-2
- Required boots, long pants, packs, water, sun protection
- Have delegates self-id for climbs (easier, not)
- Fatigue—Dehydration risk; bring plenty of water and sports drink
- Recommended: walking stick, gloves, awareness of cactus, snakes, loose rocks

## Field Activity Safety Process

### Site Safety Summary

| | | | |
|---|---|---|---|
| Field Stop Designation: | **Pleasantville Canyon Traverse and Overview** | | |
| Field Stop Category: | **Hike along abandoned road and off trail ascent/descent** | | |
| Created for (Author): | **Brushy School 03 (J. Smith and J. Black)** | **Date of last revision:** | **2-7-05 SRO** |
| Activity used for: | **Brushy School 05 (B. Green)** | | |

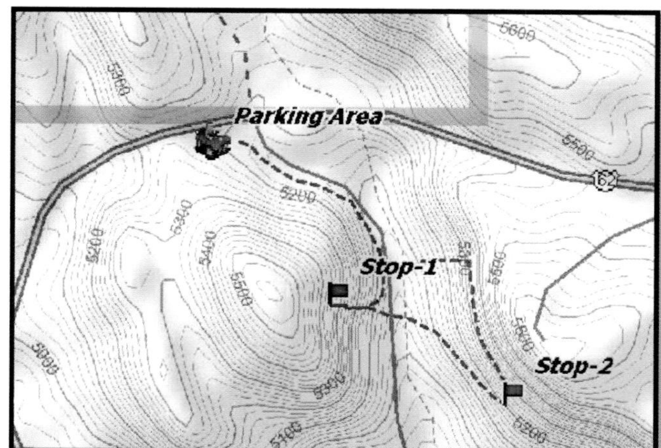

- Must be modified for the specific Field Activity. Be sure to use basic English, avoiding the use of slang, colloquial, or potentially ambiguous terms.
- To be kept by participant for reference in Activity preparation and participation.

> NOTE: The red italicized parts of the Safety Assessment form are intended as EXAMPLES and are to be replaced with Activity-specific information.

- **Participant Safety Acknowledgement Form:**
  - This form prompts each participant to provide:
    - Acknowledgement that participant has read and understands the letter and has discussed the Activity with his or her supervisor.
    - SHE-related training status and field experience
    - Requests for special course modifications due to personal conditions
    - Contact information in case of emergency
  - No Activity-specific modifications are required by the Staff before sending.
  - To be signed by participant and her or his supervisor and returned to Activity Coordinator.
- **Emergency Information and Medical Certification:**
  - This form prompts each participant to provide:
    - Participant Emergency Contact Information—personal and Organizational
    - Medical Information and Fitness Certification—includes physician's endorsement of participation for people with certain existing medical conditions.
  - No Activity-specific modifications are required by the Staff before sending.
    - To be signed, returned to Activity Coordinator, and treated as private information.
- **Guidelines for Driving Organization Vehicles:**
  - Contains requirements and protocols for operating vehicles owned or leased by the organization. Guidelines for this should be established at a relatively high level in each organization and reviewed periodically as part of the overall safety program.
  - No Activity-specific modifications are required by the Staff before sending.
  - To be read and signed by Participants willing to be a designated driver for the Activity. Returned to Activity Coordinator or her/his designee.
  - Participants may be directed to submit the *Participant Safety Acknowledgement Form* and the *Emergency Information and Medical Certification* to either the Training Contact (for Schools) or another person designated by the Activity Coordinator.

> NOTE: Completion and return of both signed forms are required for participation in the Activity.

## Review of Pre-Activity Package by Geoscience Field Safety Coordinator

The Geoscience Field Safety Coordinator or designee is expected to review the Pre-Activity Package before the Activity Owner's review.

## Review of Pre-Activity Package by Activity Owner

The Activity Owner should be given the opportunity to review the Pre-Activity Package before it is released to the participants either by Training or by the Activity Coordinator. At a minimum, he or she should receive a copy when the Package is sent to the Participants.

## Release of Pre-Activity Package to Participants

For all Field Schools, the Training Contact will send the Package to the Participants. For Field Trips and Fieldwork, the Activity Coordinator is responsible for sending the Package.

## Receive Participant Safety Acknowledgement Forms

The Participant Safety Acknowledgement Form is how participants communicate their specific needs relevant to Activity delivery, logistics, dietary restrictions, etc. Upon receipt the Coordinator, Logistics Coordinator, and appropriate other Staff must review the forms and determine if modifications to the school delivery plan, the Activity Risk Assessment, or both need to be made.

- If the assessed risk level is changed by any modifications, then it must be reviewed and approved by the appropriate level of management.
- If modifications to the delivery plan are required, then the entire Staff should meet to discuss the changes. Course modifications need to consider the safety of all participants and staff, provide an effective Field Activity experience for all, and be reasonable relative to the technical objectives of the Activity and the field sites involved (as well as conforming

to all relevant laws or regulations). For example, if three participants in a Field School are confined to wheelchairs, discussion of course delivery modifications should start with a review of the key learning objectives of the school and then consider each field site (using the Site Safety Summary sheets with their pre-existing evaluation of accessibility) within the context of the entire school. Proposed modifications to field learning activities should be discussed with the affected participants as needed and appropriate. Experience has shown that most learning objectives can be achieved with creativity and goodwill on the part of both the staff and all participants, realizing that everyone does not have to see every rock to benefit from a field school. Almost all course delivery modifications will require additional time at field sites, so the overall course schedule also needs to be reviewed and modified as appropriate. Any course modifications and alternatives considered should be documented, as they can benefit future Activities. The documentation is maintained in the GFSC Activity file for future reference.

## Participant Emergency Information and Medical Certification Forms

The information provided in these forms is to be treated as "Private" unless or until an emergency situation requires them to be accessed. They are to be opened by the Training Contact for Schools (or Activity Coordinator for Field Trips and Fieldwork) only to verify that each participant has provided the required information. The Activity Coordinator should review the forms prior to the Activity. The forms should be sealed in a distinctly marked envelope and carried each day in the Safety Watch Pack. They are to be opened in the field only in the event of an emergency and only if a Participant is unable to provide such information verbally.

> NOTE: It is the responsibility of the participant to determine his or her appropriate level of participation in any activity. Staff members *MUST NOT* use the information on these forms to limit a person's participation. The Activity Coordinator, however, still has the responsibility and authority to modify or limit any participant's activities if that participant behaves in a demonstrably unsafe manner or becomes a hazard to themselves or others.

The following forms for this section are also located on the CD-Rom accompanying this book:

Management Letter—3L
Fieldwork Letter—3L1
Safety Assessment—3M
Participant Safety Acknowledgment Form—3N
Emergency Information and Medical Certification Form—3O
Driver Safety Information (including *Guidelines for Driving Organization Vehicles*)—3P

*(text continued on page 100)*

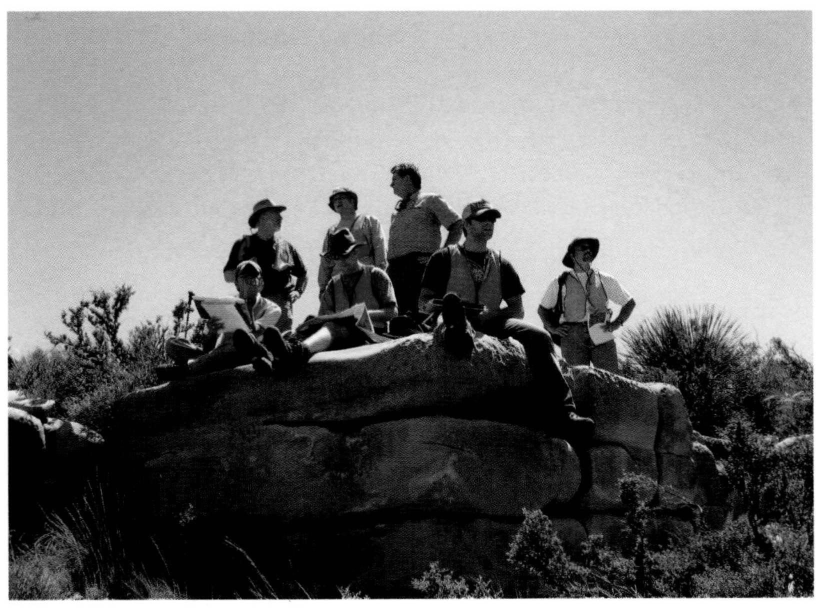

# 3L
# School or Trip Form Letter

Month Day, Year

Dear Participant,

Congratulations on your selection as a participant in the Date of School/Trip session of the Name of School/Trip. The school/trip is designed to provide a safe, educational and enjoyable experience that will enhance your career/education at this organization.

We have made several enhancements to the preparation, administration, and execution of geologic field schools/trips. These changes include providing you with more detailed information about the field portion of the school/trip and a request for any relevant medical and physical information, which are in a separate attachment. In order to participate in the school/trip, you are required to read, complete and return the attached pre-school/trip information.

The organization is concerned about your privacy rights, and does not want to exclude anyone from career/education enhancement opportunities. At the same time, the organization does not want anyone to risk their health or possible injury to themselves or others. Therefore, it is important for you to evaluate the stated risks with regard to your own personal health and safety, request reasonable modifications (accommodations) to the course delivery, and modify your participation or attendance accordingly.

Name of School/Trip Coordinator will serve as the Coordinator for this school/trip. He/She and the other school/trip staff will provide guidance on health and safety issues, but your personal commitment to safety is essential to the successful completion of the school/trip. The safety of each participant is to be the first consideration at all times and in all places. The Coordinator has the authority to dismiss participants who refuse to follow the school's/trip's safety procedures. Any such dismissal will result in an incomplete status, and will be promptly reported to the participant's line management/academic advisor.

Please take full advantage of this outstanding opportunity to learn in the Name of School/Trip, and also help contribute to its safe completion. As in the past, we welcome constructive suggestions for improvements to all aspects of the program.

Sincerely,

Appropriately high-level Leadership or Management Person (e.g., Vice President, Department Chairperson)

# 3L 1
# Fieldwork Form Letter

Date

Dear Participant,

Congratulations on your selection as a participant in this Geologic field work. The work is designed to provide a safe and worthwhile experience that will enhance your/the organization's knowledge of geologic systems.

We have made several enhancements to the preparation, administration, and execution of geologic fieldwork. These changes include providing you with more detailed information about the physical conditions of the field area and a request for any relevant medical and physical information, which are in a separate attachment. In order to participate in the fieldwork, you are required to read, complete, and return the attached pre-trip information.

***Coordinator Name*** will serve as the Field Work Coordinator. ***He/She*** and the other fieldwork staff will provide guidance on health and safety issues, but your personal commitment to safety is essential to the successful completion of the work. The safety of each participant is to be the first consideration at all times and in all places. The Field Work Coordinator has the authority to dismiss participants who refuse to follow the Field Work safety procedures. Any such dismissal will promptly reported to your line management/academic advisor.

Please take full advantage of this outstanding opportunity to learn in the field, and also help contribute to the safe completion of the work. As in the past, we welcome constructive suggestions for improvements to all aspects of the activity.

Sincerely,

*Appropriate Vice President*

## Field Activity Safety Process 3M

# Pre-Activity Safety Assessment

Activity Name: ______________________ Type: School/Trip Dates: ____________

**To: Activity Participants**

Congratulations on your opportunity to participate in this Activity! Because some or all of the Activity will take place in field locations, this letter outlines the associated health and safety issues and serves to inform you of potential hazards that need to be considered for your participation. It is important for you to evaluate the stated risks with regard to your own personal health and safety, request reasonable modifications ("accommodations") to course delivery, and modify your participation or attendance accordingly.

---

**Sections and Attachments**

The following sections and attachments outline the health and safety issues that need to be considered for your participation, as well as the measures in place to prevent and mitigate them:

- Field Safety and Health Considerations*
- Identification and Mitigation of Potential Safety Hazards*
- Guidelines for Driving Company Vehicles (attachment)
- Field Activity Safety Acknowledgment Form (attachment)
- Emergency and Medical Information Form (attachment)

* *Keep these information sheets for reference before and during the Activity*

---

**Required Actions**

- Read all sections and attachments.
- Complete and sign the **Field Activity Safety Acknowledgement form** indicating that you have reviewed and understand the health and safety material provided. Have your supervisor sign and date indicating approval.
- Review and sign the **Guidelines for Driving Organization Vehicles** if you are willing to drive during the Activity.
- Complete and sign the **Emergency and Medical Information form**.
- Return all signed forms to the Activity Coordinator or Training contact.

---

**Deadline**

**As Soon As Possible After Receipt, and no later than 4 weeks before the start of the Activity (date).** The signed Safety Acknowledgment form enables your participation in this school. Your participation will not be confirmed until you have signed and returned the required forms.

---

## Field Activity Safety Process 3M

# Pre-Activity Safety Assessment

**Questions**

Questions can be directed as follows:

| | Name | Telephone |
|---|---|---|
| **Activity Coordinator** | Name here | 123-456-7890 |

### Field Safety and Health Considerations

**Field Environmental Conditions**

Elevation in Wyoming and Texas field areas ranges from about 1500 to 2300 m (5000–7500 ft); California site are near sea level. Typical daytime temperatures are 25 to 30°C (75–85°F), but you should be prepared for temperatures from -1 to 35°C (30°F to 95°F). Brief, intense rainstorms are possible. Strong winds and blowing dust are common. (Snow is sometimes encountered in Wyoming.) Vegetation is a typical high-desert/steppe assemblage (sage, pine, cactus, greasewood), so expect to encounter thorny brush and cacti. In California poison oak is a common plant, and contact usually results in a rash.

Venomous snakes, spiders, and insects exist in the field areas but are not commonly encountered by school groups. Ticks are present locally in Wyoming and may carry disease (Rocky Mountain Fever and Lyme Disease).

**Description of Field Terrain**

The class will make hikes of short to intermediate duration (20–60 min) with mostly moderate elevation gain (10–35 m; 33–115ft) in rough, steep terrain, with thorny brush and burrs. The most strenuous day involves an hike and outcrop description exercise that covers 6 km (3.5 mi) with an elevation gain of 250 m (800 ft) during the course of about 6 hours.

## Field Activity Safety Process 3M

# Pre-Activity Safety Assessment

### Identification of Potential Safety Hazards

| | |
|---|---|
| **Slips, Trips, and Falls** | There are trip and fall hazards on ledges and loose rocks on hillsides and trails. |
| **Personal health/ hazardous conditions** | • Poor physical conditioning may lead to overexertion and severe fatigue which can exacerbate pre-existing medical conditions and contribute to accidents. As detailed in the attached form, participants with certain serious medical conditions must check with their physician or health services department prior to attending this school. *See attached* ***Emergency Contact and Medical Certification*** *form.*<br>• Allergic reactions to insect bite or plant puncture wound.<br>• Heat-related illness/dehydration.<br>• Sunburn. |
| **Motor vehicle hazards** | • Persons unaccustomed to driving in the U.S. (on the right hand side of the road) or on unpaved roads should not consider driving during this Activity.<br>• Flat tires are a common potential hazard.<br>• Fatigue, distractions, and inattention during driving are potential hazards.<br>• *Fuel spills during fueling are a potential hazard.* |

# Field Activity Safety Process 3M

## Pre-Activity Safety Assessment

### Mitigation of Safety Hazards

**Overview**

Each person is primarily responsible for his or her own safe conduct, as well as contributing to the welfare of the entire group. Every morning and at each Field Site, the Activity Coordinator will brief the participants on the expected and potential hazardous situations and conditions.

- If you are not comfortable participating in any of the particular activities for any reason, you are encouraged to notify the Coordinator or other Staff member. There are no negative implications for this decision.
- If you become uncomfortable with the actions or behavior of your fellow participants, please notify the Coordinator, other Staff member, or the Geoscience Field Safety Coordinator. Your concerns will be kept confidential and actions will be taken to remedy the situation.
- If you become uncomfortable with the actions or behavior of one of the Staff members, please contact the Geoscience Field Safety Coordinator at the earliest convenient time. Your concerns will be kept confidential and actions will be taken to remedy the situation.

The Geoscience Field Safety Coordinator, name? can be reached at **123-456-7890**, or by email at ***gfsc@null.net?***

Following are some of the typical safety practices that will be implemented.

**Trip and fall hazards**

- **Sturdy hiking boots***—Boots with Vibram-type soles with good tread and leather uppers or equivalently sturdy material capable of providing protection against thorny brush, cactus spines and sharp rocks **are required. Any participant without the required hiking boots will not be allowed to enter field sites.** Please contact the School Coordinator if you have any questions regarding the field-boot policy.
- **Long pants are strongly recommended on hiking days**
- ***Diligent care and attentiveness while traversing field pathways will reduce the occurrence of trips and falls.***
- *Tennis shoes, trainers or other athletic shoes are acceptable footwear for select hikes along the beach in coastal California. Be aware that these shoes might get wet.*
- Reckless behavior in the field (running and jumping over gullies, etc.) or wandering away from the group is unacceptable.

## Field Activity Safety Process 3M

# Pre-Activity Safety Assessment

**Personal health hazardous conditions**

- **Candidates should determine their ability to handle short periods (20–60 minutes) of high exertion at relatively high altitudes, which are required to access some of the field localities. Vertical change in elevation will be 250 m (800 ft) or less at base elevations of 1500 m (5000 ft).**
- Persons under medical care or taking daily medications are advised to consult with their physician or health services department prior to committing to participate in the school. It would also be helpful to alert the Activity Coordinator of any special medications you may be taking before any emergency situation arises.
- Persons with known dangerous allergies to insect bites, foods, etc. should make such allergies known to the Activity Coordinator so that the appropriate care can be taken of you in the event of an emergency.
- Sun block, insect repellant, and proper clothing are needed to reduce the chance of sunburn, insect bites, and overexposure.

---

**Motor vehicle hazards**

- **Organization personnel driving Organization-provided vehicles are required to take defensive driving training. This, or a similar driver education program, is strongly recommended for all persons wishing to drive field vehicles.** (Consult your SHE group for your organization's specific requirements.)
- **All Participants should pay careful attention to periodic briefings by the School Staff on potentially hazardous conditions associated with use of the vehicles.**
- Participants will wear high-visibility safety vests when working along busy roads.
- Take time to familiarize yourself with the vehicle and routes before setting out.
- Follow the procedures on the ***Guidelines for Driving Organization Vehicles*** and ***Driver Safety Briefing*** forms.
- Documented safety procedures on the changing of flat tires and fueling of vehicles must be followed.

## Field Activity Safety Process 3N

# Safety Acknowledgement

Field Activity: ______________________ Dates: __________

I certify that I have read and understand the content of the Pre-Activity Safety Assessment that describes the conditions and potential hazards that may be encountered during the Activity. I have completed and forwarded the separate ***Emergency Information and Medical Certification*** form to the Activity Coordinator. I understand the safety precautions that I need to take to minimize the risk to myself and other participants in the Activity. I agree to follow the required safety guidelines and briefings and certify, to the best of my knowledge, that I am physically capable of participating in this Activity. *I consent to the release of the information herein to Activity Staff for the purpose of preparing for and conducting the Field Work/Activity and to the retention of this Acknowledgment by the Activity Coordinator so long as evidence of the consents and acknowledgments provided herein are required.*

Signature of participant: ______________________ Date: __________

Name (printed): ______________________

*I have discussed the objectives of this Activity and the associated safety and health issues identified in the pre-trip letter with the participant and approve his/her participation:*

Signature of Supervisor: ______________________ Date: __________

Name (printed): ______________________

***Background Information:*** Please provide the following information to assist the Activity Staff in making preparations for the Field Work.

Dietary Restrictions of Dangerous Allergies (including food allergies):

______________________

______________________

Do you require any modifications to the Activity methods or activities to participate? (due to, for example, limited mobility/hearing/sight, fear of heights, plant or insect allergies, medical conditions (heart trouble, breathing problems, diabetes, etc.), pregnancy, etc.). Do you require any special emergency response preparations (e.g., medications requiring cold storage)?

☐ No ☐ Yes (specify below)

______________________

______________________

What Safety, Health, and environmental training do you have:

| | Subject | Course Name | Date of Completion |
|---|---|---|---|
| | First Aid | | |
| | CPR | | |
| | AED | | |
| | Defensive Driving | | |
| | Water Safety | | |
| | Small Craft Safety | | |
| | Other | | |

**Briefly** describe your relevant experience in field activities:

______________________

______________________

*(more, over)*

## Field Activity Safety Process 3N

# Safety Acknowledgement

Field Activity: ______________________ Dates: __________

Participant Name: ______________________ Date of Birth: __________

**Emergency Personal Contact:**

Name: ______________________ Relationship: __________

Telephone: Day: __________ Evening: __________ Mobile: __________

**Alternate Personal Contact:**

Name: ______________________ Relationship: __________

Telephone: Day: __________ Evening: __________ Mobile: __________

***Organization Information:***

Organization Unit: ______________________ City: __________

Emergency Contact (name): ______________________ Position: __________

Telephone: Day: __________ Evening: __________ E-mail: __________

**Alternate Organization Contact:**

Emergency Contact (name): ______________________ Position: __________

Telephone: Day: __________ Evening: __________ E-mail: __________

**Return this signed acknowledgment to the Activity Coordinator (Name here) upon completion:**

Via fax to 123-456-7890

Field Activity Safety Process 3O

# Emergency Information and Medical Certification

***Personal Information:***

Name: ______________________ Date of Birth: ______________

Field Activity: ______________________ Dates: ______________

The following information may be critical to caring for you in case of an injury or sudden illness during the Activity. It will be used only in the event of an emergency, and only if you are unable to communicate this information to those treating you. This form will be destroyed at the conclusion of the Activity.

***Personal Health/Accident Insurance:***

Company: ______________________ Policy/ID Number: ______________

***Known Dangerous Allergies (please list):*** (e.g. medicine, food, plant, animal, insect toxin):

______________________________________________

***Miscellaneous:***

I normally wear/use: ☐ Contact Lenses ☐ Dentures ☐ Other (list):

______________________________________________

***I hereby authorize release of the information herein to medical personnel in case of emergency:***

______________________ ______________

Signature Date

Stop here unless the Medical Conditions below apply to you.

***Medical Certification:***

Please describe any medical condition currently requiring special care, medication, or diet that can adversely affect or limit your participation in the activities described in the overview letter. These may include, but not be limited to limited mobility/hearing/sight, fear of heights, dangerous allergies, medical conditions other than those listed below, and pregnancy.*

______________________________________________

______________________________________________

______________________________________________

______________________________________________

______________________________________________

☐ The following conditions require a licensed physician or nurse practitioner to certify your fitness to participate in the Activity:

- ☐ Asthma
- ☐ Bleeding disorders
- ☐ Convulsions/seizures
- ☐ Diabetes
- ☐ Fainting Spells
- ☐ Heart Trouble
- ☐ High blood pressure

**Please consult your organization's Medical and Occupational Health group if you have any questions.*

Health-care provider's statement: ***I have examined this patient and certify that the existence of the conditions checked above do not prohibit him/her from participating in the activities described in the Pre-Activity Safety Assessment.***

***Signature :*** ______________________ ***Date:*** ______________

***Name (printed):*** ______________________

## Field Activity Safety Process 3P

# Driver Safety Briefing Sheet

| Driving Preparation/Vehicle Inspection Checklist: | | |
|---|---|---|
| ❑ **P**lan Your Route<br>■ Check Map<br>■ Review Plan<br>❑ **A**djust:<br>■ Seat/Seat Belt<br>■ Steering Wheel<br>■ Mirrors | ❑ **L**ocate Controls for:<br>■ Lights<br>■ Wipers/washer<br>■ Heating/AC<br>■ Mirrors<br>■ Horn<br>■ Windows/Locks | ❑ **N**ote/Check Condition of:<br>■ Brakes<br>■ Steering<br>■ Tires<br>■ Lights<br>■ Wipers/Washers |

**Safety Reminders/Instructions:**

- Check tires before re-entering highway from unpaved road.
- Do not use communications devices while driving—let the front seat passenger talk.
- Make sure all your passengers are in the vehicle.
- Lock all doors before leaving.
- Drive with headlights on.
- Be extra careful when backing, use a spotter as needed.
- Report problems to trip leader.
- **Buckle Up and Drive Safely.**

**Convoy Protocol:**

- Activity leaders in lead vehicle. Instructor or logistics coordinator in the last vehicle.
- Review route, intermediate stops/gathering points, final destination, and approx. arrival times before departing. Intermediate gathering points will be about 1 hour's drive apart.
- Maintain radio contact between vehicles. DO NOT act unsafely just to maintain visual contact on the highway or in city traffic!
- Drive at posted speed limit or slower if conditions dictate.
- Do not pass any other vehicles in the convoy unless directed to do so by Leader.
- On unpaved roads: Maintain visual contact with vehicles just in front of and behind you.
- Maintain safe distance between vehicles (at the very least 2-second rule).
- If your vehicle becomes separated from the group or develops mechanical problems find a safe place to pull off the road and contact leader.

**Tire changing protocol:**

- Only field trip leaders or their designates will change tires. Experienced tire changers only.
- Tire changer and assistant should wear reflective vest if passing vehicles are a possibility.
- Park vehicle on firm level surface.
- Place traffic warning devices as necessary.
- Review safe work practices for operation.
- Block the wheels and set the parking brake before jacking vehicle.
- No one allowed in vehicle when on the jack.
- Tire changer and assistant use appropriate personal protective equipment.
- Use proper lifting techniques: use legs, not back.
- Use appropriate lug wrench tool (consider use of 4-way tire tool).
- Never place body under a vehicle supported by a jack.

## Field Activity Safety Process 3P1

# Guidelines for Driving Organization Vehicles

Please read the following guidelines that must be met before driving any organization vehicles. Your signature indicates that you have met and agreed to the guidelines as listed below:

1. An **Organization Vehicle** is defined as "any vehicle that is owned, rented, leased, or otherwise provided to associates for use in conducting organization business."
2. An **authorized driver** is any individual that has been authorized to drive a Company Vehicle. In order for a driver to be considered **authorized**, the individual should meet the following standards:
   A. Possess a valid driver's license for the type of vehicle to be driven that is recognized by the country or local authority where the vehicle is to be operated.
   B. Strongly recommended that the driver should have taken and passed a government-authorized Defensive Driving Course, or equivalent for non-U.S.A. organizations, within the last three years.
3. Vehicle operator should thoroughly inspect the assigned vehicle prior to initial use and prior to first use each day thereafter for obviously unsafe conditions (lights, brakes, windshield wipers) or damage. Operators must immediately report vehicles that are damaged or in an unsafe condition.
4. A member assigned an Organization Vehicle is responsible for ensuring that only authorized drivers are permitted to drive the vehicle and that it is operated in compliance with organization safety policy and operating procedures.
5. Seat belts, both lap and shoulder, must be worn by the driver and all passengers when the vehicle is in motion.
6. An accident involving an Organization Vehicle, or privately owned vehicle occurring during the accomplishment of Organization business, must be reported according to organization accident reporting guidelines (work with Activity Coordinator to facilitate this).
7. Vehicle operators must always be familiar with and strictly observe all applicable traffic laws. All traffic citations should be reported to their supervisor and are the financial responsibility of the driver. The driver of an Organization Vehicle **must not** exceed the maximum posted speed limit and **must** always drive at a speed suitable for the condition of the vehicle, road, traffic, and weather.

   Where vision is restricted, the driver **must** slow to a speed that will permit the safe negotiation of curves, hills, or intersections.
8. The use of a Organization Vehicle while under the influence of alcohol or drugs, including prescription drugs that may impair the ability of the driver to operate the vehicle, is strictly prohibited.
9. If an authorized driver receives a suspension, probation, cancellation, or disqualification of his/her driver's license, he/she must inform their supervisor immediately.
10. The transporting of hitchhikers is strictly prohibited.
11. Hazardous materials (e.g. flammables, corrosives, explosives, compressed gases, etc.) must not be transported in a Organization Vehicle unless they have been packaged as prescribed by applicable state and federal regulations. (Guidance on packaging and hazardous material transportation documentation is available via contact with the organization's SHE group (123-456-7890)). The vehicle operator **must** be informed before the hazardous material is loaded for transport.
12. The engines of unattended vehicles **should** normally be turned off. However, there are situations when the vehicle may be left running for a short period of time. When an unattended vehicle is left running, the parking brake **must** be set and at least one wheel **must** be chocked.
13. The use of cellular telephones by the driver while driving is not permitted (even with a "bands-free" device), except in immediate emergency situations.

Signature ______________________ Date ____________

Name (printed) ______________________

## SECTION 3.6: SAFETY, HEALTH, AND ENVIRONMENT (SHE) PLAN DEVELOPMENT

A Safety, Health, and Environment Plan (SHE Plan) must be developed for each Activity. In it, the Staff summarizes planned activities and documents preparations to carry them out safely. The Plan is to be used for reference during the Activity and also provides the Activity Owner an overview of the preparation. The SHE Plan template (form 3Q, below) includes a cover page, the ***Activity Preparation Approval Form,*** which is used to document preparations and obtain management approval to proceed.

### 3.6.1. Field Schools, Field Trips, and Fieldwork

For Field Schools and most Field Trips and Fieldwork, an Activity-specific SHE Plan is to be developed using the attached SHE Plan template. (A sample SHE Plan for a Field School is also attached for reference.) Following is a brief description of the level of information that should be documented in each section of the Plan.

- **Locations and Staff:** List the general locations in which the Activity will be operated, i.e. cities or towns and state or province. List all Activity Staff including Instructors and safety-specific personnel under "Additional Staff."
- **Activity Locations:** At a minimum, list the general areas or first and last places to be visited each day. For Schools or Trips, list the specific sites to be visited each day or attach a detailed agenda—for either option, use the title of each site used on the Site Summary Sheet. For Fieldwork, be as specific as necessary to allow an accurate picture of the proposed field operations—local landmark names are useful, such as "along the west side of Delaney Rim," "near junction of Route 9A and US 15," or "Nine-Mile Canyon near Argyle Canyon."
- **Brief Description of Activities:** Provide an overview of the activities to be undertaken, with specific mention of the potentially more serious hazards associated with the Activity. Normally this is extracted from Introduction section of the ***Pre-Activity Safety Assessment*** form and the ***Risk Assessment Summary Report.***
- **Logistics Overview:**
    - List the hotels or motels that will be used, along with dates and contact telephone numbers.
    - List the number and types of vehicles to be used, along with the company(ies) from which they will be rented or chartered.
    - List any air transportation that is arranged by the Activity for all Staff and Participants. Do not list personal travel arrangements.
- **Staff/Activity Communications:** List the numbers of the cellular phones and satellite phones to be carried by Activity Staff. Include any special access numbers required.
- **Identified Hazards:** Attach a copy of the ***Risk Assessment Summary Report*** and ***Site Summary Sheets*** as appropriate. **Do not list the hazards in the SHE Plan.**

■ **Equipment:**
- List Personal Protective Equipment (PPE) required of and recommended to Staff and Participants. For Schools or Trips, these lists are developed during the Risk Assessment process (Section 2) and reviewed during session-specific preparations (Section 3). For Fieldwork, start with the list on the ***Generic Fieldwork Risk Assessment Summary Report*** and modify as determined during the preparation process.
- Indicate the First Aid and Safety Equipment to be carried, including quantities where applicable. Modify the list as determined during preparation for the circumstances of the specific Activity.

> NOTE: Do not list the contents of standard-issue First-Aid kits.

- List any tools to be used, both Activity-supplied and personal. These may include hand tools such as hammers and shovels, and power tools.

■ **SHE-Related Training:** Either fill in these tables by using information returned on ***Participant Safety Acknowledgement*** form or enter "See attached ***Participant Safety Acknowledgement*** forms" (this is a particularly useful option for large groups).

> NOTE: A training waiver is required for any Staff not having current certification in any of the required training. Attach a copy of any waivers to SHE Plan.

**The following form for this section is also located on the CD-Rom accompanying this book:**
**SHE Plan Template—3Q**

*(text continued on page 107)*

## Field Activity Safety Process 3Q

# Activity SHE PLAN

Activity Name: ______________________ Dates: __________

The processes listed below are to be completed prior to the beginning of all Field Activities. The checklist is a tool with which the Activity Coordinator documents completion and obtains approval from the Activity Owner to proceed with the Field Activity.

### All Field Activities

- ❑ **Review existing Risk Assessment(s) and upgrade as necessary—or conduct a new one.**
- ❑ **Review Pre-trip documents including Safety Acknowledgement & Medical Release**
- ❑ **Review and Address Participants' Special Needs**
- ❑ **Review the Field Activity SHE\ERP Plan**
- ❑ **Conduct a Pre-Activity Safety Review Meeting**

### Field Trips and Field Work only

- ❑ **Review the host organization's SHE Plan and develop bridging document or develop original SHE Plan**

### Travel and Transportation Documentation

- ❑ **Non-scheduled/Charter transportation**—approval form attached *(approval varies by organization).*
- ❑ **Foreign Travel**—approval form attached *(approval process varies by organization).*

### Additional Documentation Requirements

(The indicated additional documents are attached if appropriate to this Activity)

☐ Waiver Approval Form ☐ Special Training Certificates ☐ Permits ☐ Third-party contracts

☐ Other (list) ______________________

### Assessed Risk Level, Endorsement, and Approval

**The assessed Risk Level for this Activity is: ☐ Lower ☐ Intermediate ☐ Higher**

**Activity Coordinator:** ______________ Submitted ______________ **Date:** __________

**SHE Representative:** ______________ Endorsed ______________ **Date:** __________

**Field Safety Coordinator:** ______________ Endorsed ______________ **Date:** __________

**Activity Owner:** ______________ Approved ______________ **Date:** __________

### Post-Activity Documentation

☐ Field Activity "follow up form" (attached). Date completed and filed: __________

## Field Activity Safety Process 3Q

# Activity SHE PLAN

Activity Name: ______________________ Dates: __________

### *LOCATIONS AND STAFF*

**Location(s):** ______________________

**Coordinator:** __________ **Logistics Coordinator:** __________

**Additional Staff:** ______________________

| Date | Activity Locations |
|---|---|
| | |
| | |
| | |
| | |
| | |
| | |
| | |
| | |
| | |

### *BRIEF DESCRIPTION OF ACTIVITIES (identify the higher risk hazards):*

| General: |
|---|
| |

### *Logistics Overview*

| Hotel | City | Telephone | Dates |
|---|---|---|---|
| | | | |
| | | | |
| | | | |
| | | | |
| | | | |
| | | | |

| Ground Transportation | City | # and type of vehicles |
|---|---|---|
| | | |
| | | |

### *AIR TRANSPORTATION (arranged as part of Activity)**

| Date: | | Airline and Flight Number: | | | | | |
|---|---|---|---|---|---|---|---|
| From: | | To: | | Dep. Time: | | Arr. Time: | |

*Complete and attach approved **Aircraft Approval Form**: if helicopter or charter aircraft are to be used.

### *STAFF/ACTIVITY COMMUNICATIONS*

| Cell-Phone Numbers: | |
|---|---|
| Satellite Phone Numbers: | |

# Field Activity Safety Process 3Q

## Activity SHE PLAN

Activity Name: ______________________ Dates: __________

### *IDENTIFIED HAZARDS*

*(See Risk Assessment Summary Report)*

### *EQUIPMENT*

**Personal Protective Equipment (PPE):**

| Required | Recommended |
|---|---|
| | |
| | |
| | |

**First Aid / Safety Equipment**

| | | | |
|---|---|---|---|
| | Standard-issue First-Aid Kits (#) | | Satellite Telephones (#) |
| | Field Radios (#) | | |
| | Emergency Road Markers | | |
| | Pin-Flags/Surveyors Tape | | |
| | | | |

# = Indicate quantity

**Tools to be used in field:**

**List:** None

### *SHE-RELATED TRAINING*

Staff—(Review appropriate training database(s))

| Staff Member* | Required | | | Other (list)** | |
|---|---|---|---|---|---|
| | First Aid** | CPR** | Def. Driving** | | |
| | | | | | |
| | | | | | |
| | | | | | |
| | | | | | |

Attendees: (fill in below or attach separate sheet)

| Attendee* | Affiliate | First Aid/ CPR** | Defensive Driving** | Other (list)** |
|---|---|---|---|---|
| | | | | |
| | | | | |

*** Indicate drivers with (D) after name**
**** Indicate the date that training was last taken.**

### EMERGENCY PREPAREDNESS AND RESPONSE

***(Refer to the Emergency Response Plan, form 3J, above.)***

# Activity SHE Plan

**Activity Name:** Example Field Activity **Dates:** September 12–24, 2004

The processes listed below are to be completed prior to the beginning of all Field Activities. The checklist is a tool with which the Activity Coordinator documents completion and obtains approval from the Activity Owner to proceed with the Field Activity.

## All Field Activities

- ❑ **Review existing Risk Assessment(s) and upgrade as necessary—or conduct a new one.**
- ❑ **Review pre-trip documents including Safety Acknowledgement and Medical Release.**
- ❑ **Review and address Participants' Special Needs.**
- ❑ **Review the Field Activity SHE\ERP Plan.**
- ❑ **Conduct a Pre-activity safety review meeting.**

## Field Trips and Field Work only

- ❑ **Review the host organization's SHE Plan and develop bridging document or develop original SHE Plan.**

## Travel and Transportation Documentation

- ❑ Non-scheduled/Charter transportation—**Approval form attached *(approval varies by organization).***
- ❑ Foreign Travel—**Approval form attached *(approval process varies by organization).***

## Additional Documentation Requirements

**(The indicated additional documents are attached if appropriate to this Activity)**

☐ Waiver Approval Form ☐ Special Training Certificates ☐ Permits ☐ Third-party contracts

☐ Other (list) ______________________

## Assessed Risk Level, Endorsement, and Approval

**The assessed Risk Level for this Activity is: ☐ Lower ☐ Intermediate ☐ Higher**

| | | | |
|---|---|---|---|
| **Activity Coordinator:** | *Submitted* | **Date:** | |
| **SHE Representative:** | *Endorsed* | **Date:** | |
| **Field Safety Coordinator:** | *Endorsed* | **Date:** | |
| **Activity Owner:** | *Approved* | **Date:** | |

## Post-Activity Documentation

☐ Field Activity 'follow up form' (attached). Date completed and filed: ____________

# Activity SHE Plan

**Activity Name:** Example Field Activity **Dates:** September 12–24, 2004

## LOCATIONS AND STAFF

**Location(s):** Utah and Colorado

**Coordinator:** John Smith **Logistics Coordinator:** Jane Black

**Additional Staff:** Bill Green, Staff #4

| Date | Activity Locations |
|---|---|
| | For details refer to the attached itinerary |
| Sept. 12 | Salt Lake City, Utah |
| Sept. 13 | Levan, Utah Gunnison, Utah |
| Sept. 14–16 | Emery, Utah |
| Sept. 17–18 | Helper, Utah |
| Sept. 19 | San Rafael, Utah |
| Sept. 20 | Moab, Utah |
| Sept. 21–24 | Grand Junction, Colorado |

### *BRIEF DESCRIPTION OF ACTIVITIES (identify the higher risk hazards):*

**General:** 1) Drive to outcrops on paved and gravel roads; 2) Hike along old mining trails or hike on paths to vantage points to observe outcrops; 3) Either describe outcrops or interpret photomontages; 4) Discuss relevant points of outcrop exposures; 5) Return to vehicles.

## *Logistics Overview*

| Hotel | City | Telephone | Dates |
|---|---|---|---|
| Marriott City Center | Salt Lake City, Utah | 123-456-7890 | Sept. 11–12, 2004 |
| Best Western Salina | Salina, Utah | 123-456-7890 | Sept. 13, 2004 |
| Wonderland Inn | Torrey, Utah | 123-456-7890 | Sept. 14, 2004 |
| Holiday Inn | Price, Utah | 123-456-7890 | Sept. 15–17, 2004 |
| Best Western River Terrace | Green River, Utah | 123-456-7890 | Sept. 18–19, 2004 |
| Best Western CanyonLandsInn | Moab, Utah | 123-456-7890 | Sept. 20–21, 2004 |
| Hawthorn Suites | Grand Junction, Colorado | 123-456-7890 | Sept. 22–24, 2004 |

| Ground Transportation | City | Number and type of vehicles |
|---|---|---|
| Budget Rental Cars | Grand Junction, CO | 8 (eight) SUVs; all are 4-wheel drive |

### *AIR TRANSPORTATION (ACTIVITY ARRANGED)**

| Date: | | Airline (Flight): | | | |
|---|---|---|---|---|---|
| From: | | To: | | Departure Time: | | Arrival Time: | |

* Complete and attach approved **Aircraft Approval Form** if helicopter or charter aircraft are to be used.

### *STAFF / ACTIVITY COMMUNICATIONS*

| Cell-Phone Numbers: | 123-456-7890 (John Smith) |
|---|---|
| Satellite Phone Numbers: | 123-456-7890 (Jane Black) |

# Activity Preparation Approval Form

**Activity Name:** Example Field Activity **Dates:** September 12–24, 2004

***IDENTIFIED HAZARDS***

(See Attached Risk Assessment Summary Report (e.g. URC Form 2-2))

EQUIPMENT

## Personal Protective Equipment (PPE)

| Required | Recommended |
|---|---|
| Vibram-soled, sturdy hiking boots with a leather top or suitable material | Hat, long pants, sun screen, rain gear, walking sticks |

### First Aid/Safety Equipment

| | | | |
|---|---|---|---|
| X | Standard-issue First-Aid Kits (#) 1 | X | Satellite Telephones (#) 1 |
| X | Field Radios (#) 3 | | |
| X | Emergency Road Markers | | |
| X | Pin-Flags / Surveyors Tape | | |

# = Indicate quantity

### Tools

| **List:** None |
|---|

*SHE-RELATED TRAINING*

Staff – (Review available training database(s))

| Staff Member* | Required | | | Other (list)** | |
|---|---|---|---|---|---|
| | First Aid** | CPR** | Def. Driving** | | |
| John Smith | Feb. 2003 | Feb. 2003 | Feb. 2004 | AED (2-03) | When Help is Delayed (7-04) |
| Jane Black | Feb. 2003 | Feb. 2003 | Oct. 2003 | | |
| Bill Green | Aug. 2004 | Aug. 2004 | June 2002 | | When Help is Delayed (8-04) |
| Paul Brown | July 2004 | Feb. 2003 | Feb. 2004 | AED (2-03) | When Help is Delayed (7-04) |

Attendees: (fill in below or attach separate sheet)

| Attendee* | Affiliate | First Aid/ CPR** | Defensive Driving** | Other (list)** |
|---|---|---|---|---|
| Attendee 1 | EMDC | | Mar. 2004 | |
| Attendee 2 | EMDC | | | |
| Attendee 3 | EMEC | | Nov. 2001 | |
| Attendee 4 | EMEC | | | |
| Attendee 5 | EMEC | 2003 | | AED 2003 |
| Attendee 6 | EMPC | | | |
| Attendee 7 | EMPC-US | | Dec. 2003 | |
| Etc. | EMV | | | |

*** Indicate drivers with (D) after name**

** Indicate the date that training was last taken.

**EMERGENCY PREPAREDNESS AND RESPONSE**

**(Refer to the Emergency Response Plan above)**

## SECTION 3.7: FIELD ACTIVITIES OPERATED BY OTHERS (OBO)

The term "OBO Activity" includes trips or schools sponsored by universities or industry groups, such as AAPG or SEG, which are not organized or led by personnel from the participant's home organization. Due to the fact that the home organization has no control over the preparation, organization, or execution of these activities, individual participants are charged with the majority of their own safety preparations. **Any Field Activity that is led by a home organization member must follow the procedures for "Field Trips" outlined previously in this manual.** Trips organized or arranged by the home organization but led by consultants need to follow the full procedure for Field Trips.

Each Participant in an OBO Activity needs to do the following things, using a copy of this page to document his or her preparations:

- Complete the attached *Potential Hazards Register* (form 3R, below) using the trip description, trip itinerary, and other information that you have about the trip. Check all the hazards that apply so that you can discuss them, along with likely risks, with your supervisor. Background information on the hazards is available for the *Potential Hazards Register* in standard references or on the Web. If more information is needed, contact the activity organizers for their plans that address safety, health, and emergency response. Review for completeness (compared to SHE plan and ERP templates in this section above). If you have unresolved issues, contact the organizers for more information and plan your participation accordingly.
- Create a personal safety plan using the attached *Personal Safety Planner* (form 3S, below). Please check off the safety considerations that you propose to follow to either prevent the hazard or mitigate the risks identified on the Hazard Register. Review the PPE Recommendations information to determine what items are appropriate for your situation.
- Complete an *Emergency Medical Information* (form 3T, below) form. Inform the OBO Activity organizer upon your arrival where the form will be kept in case access to the information is needed.
- For OBO Activities outside your home country, ensure that you have reviewed your organization's emergency medical response system information and are carrying a reference card with contact numbers. In particular, investigate coverage for medical treatment, prescription medications, and emergency repatriation. Your organization's medical or safety group can provide more information.
- Obtain required permissions for Foreign Travel and Non-Scheduled Chartered Transportation, as appropriate.
- Discuss your plans and preparations with your supervisor at least 1 week prior to your departure.

Your management expects that you will conduct yourself in accordance with your Personal Safety Plan throughout your field trip and make safety your first priority. You are expected to decline participation in any part of the Activity that you judge to be unsafe. Furthermore, you are expected to recognize your own individual limitations and not participate in activities that would exceed those limitations.

**The following forms for this section are also located on the CD-Rom accompanying this book:**
**Potential Hazard Register—3R**
**Personal Safety Planner—3S**
**Emergency Medical Information Form—3T**

*Field Activity Safety Manual* **3R**

# PERSONAL SAFETY PLANNER

**Instructions**: Below you will find a list of prevention/mitigation steps for hazards (risks) that could be encountered on field trips. Using the hazards that you identified on the Potential Hazards Register, check off and consider the prevention and mitigation actions that you intend to take to keep yourself safe on the field excursion. Discuss the identified hazards, the Emergency Response Procedures, and your planned prevention and mitigation actions with your supervisor prior to participating in the trip.

==========================================================================

*I certify that I understand the conditions and potential hazards that may be encountered during the Activity. I understand the safety precautions that I need to take to minimize the risk to myself and other participants in the Activity. I understand the Emergency Response Procedures for the activity. I agree to follow the required safety guidelines and briefings and certify, to the best of my knowledge, that I am physically capable of participating in this Activity.*

Signature of participant: ______________________________ Date: ______________

Name (printed): ______________________________________________

*I have discussed the objectives of this Activity and the associated safety and health issues identified in the pre-trip material with the participant and approve his/her participation:*

Signature of Supervisor: ______________________________ Date: ______________

Name (printed): ______________________________________________

==========================================================================

## Recommended Prevention/Mitigation Actions
## Vehicle Operation

| | Hazard Area | Event | Prevention and Mitigation Measures to Implement |
|---|---|---|---|
| ❑ | Equipment failure (vehicles)<br>1. Land<br>2. Water | Mechanical failure resulting in collision:<br>1. Land vehicles (brakes, steering, tire nuts, flat tire)<br>2. Boats (rudders, motors, hull) | - Screened rental or charter agency<br>- Vehicle inspection<br>- Defensive Driving or Watercraft Certification<br>- Driving or Boating experience<br>- Emergency Response Plan |
| ❑ | Limited sight lines | Collision due to fog or winding roads | - Defensive Driving<br>- Go/No-Go criteria<br>- Emergency Response Plan<br>- Alcohol/drug policy<br>- Safety and personal awareness |
| ❑ | Foul weather | Heavy rain | - Field activity scheduling<br>- Weather watch<br>- Go/No-Go criteria<br>- Emergency Response Plan |

## *Field Activity Safety Manual* *3R*

| | Hazard Area | Event | Prevention and Mitigation Measures to Implement |
|---|---|---|---|
| ❑ | Foreign driving | Collision due to inexperience with opposite side driving or foreign country procedures | - Use of experienced local drivers in foreign countries<br>- Defensive Driving<br>- Go/No-Go criteria<br>- Emergency Response Plan<br>- Alcohol/drug policy<br>- Safety and personal awareness |
| ❑ | Exiting boat to shore onto slick surfaces | Participant slips between boat and shore, sustains cuts or blunt trauma injury | - First Aid and CPR training<br>- Fieldwork team orientation and assistance<br>- Boat captain's experience<br>- Wear PFD until on land<br>- Emergency Response Plan |
| ❑ | All other driving hazards | Minor accidents | - Defensive Driving<br>- Emergency Response Plan<br>- Alcohol/drug policy<br>- Safety and personal awareness |

## On land activities

| | Hazard Area | Event | Prevention and Mitigation Measures to Implement |
|---|---|---|---|
| ❑ | Temperature extremes—hot | High temperature and humidity, participant suffers heat stroke (progresses beyond unrecognized heat exhaustion) | - Time of year for scheduled field activity<br>- Time of day for particular field activity<br>- Safety and personal awareness<br>- Proper PPE for field activity (clothing, hat, etc.)<br>- Adequate hydration<br>- First Aid training<br>- Group interaction and ongoing assessment |
| ❑ | Temperature extremes—cold | Participant gets wet during course of work during relatively cool weather, progresses into mild hypothermia, and suffers accident due to impaired judgment/coordination | - Time of year for scheduled field activity<br>- Time of day for particular field activity<br>- Safety and personal awareness<br>- Proper PPE for field activity (clothing, hat, etc.)<br>- Adequate hydration<br>- First Aid training<br>- Group interaction and ongoing assessment of fellow participants<br>- Arctic survival training (as appropriate) |

## *Field Activity Safety Manual* *3R*

| | Hazard Area | Event | Prevention and Mitigation Measures to Implement |
|---|---|---|---|
| ❑ | Uneven /slippery walking surface | Participant slips, falls, and fractures a bone, sustains lacerations, or is subject to a blunt trauma injury | - Safety and personal awareness<br>- Proper PPE—footwear<br>- First Aid training<br>- Walking stick<br>- Appropriate route selection<br>- Group interaction and ongoing assessment of fellows<br>- Awareness of physical limitations<br>- Reasonable pacing of physical exertion<br>- Reasonable work schedule to avoid fatigue<br>- Schedule work during daylight hours, remembering time to hike out.<br>- Make sure backpacks are properly balanced and not overloaded |
| ❑ | Sharp objects | Participant accidentally lacerates self on sharp rock, pierced by cactus spine, or scratches eye on branch | - Safety and personal awareness<br>- Proper PPE (eye protection, long pants and long sleeved shirt, gloves, proper footwear)<br>- First aid training<br>- Walking stick<br>- Route selection<br>- Reasonable pacing of physical exertion<br>- Reasonable work schedule to avoid fatigue |
| ❑ | Heights/drop offs | Participant falls from height and sustains a major injury | - Safety and personal awareness<br>- Proper PPE (Footwear)<br>- First Aid training<br>- Walking stick<br>- Route selection<br>- Stay away from edge (3m/10-foot rule)<br>- Awareness of physical limitations<br>- Reasonable pacing of physical exertion<br>- Reasonable work schedule to avoid fatigue<br>- Group interaction and ongoing assessment |
| ❑ | Falling objects | Participant gets hit on head by falling object dislodged by other member of party | - Safety and personal awareness<br>- Proper PPE (hard hat for overhangs and loose rock areas)<br>- First Aid training<br>- Route selection<br>- Communication among field party<br>- Awareness of stability of outcrop face, especially when digging for samples<br>- Awareness of others in area not part of field party<br>- Time of year—avoid spring thaw, fall freeze and breakup<br>- Awareness of changing weather (winds, rain, frosts) |

## *Field Activity Safety Manual* *3R*

| | Hazard Area | Event | Prevention and Mitigation Measures to Implement |
|---|---|---|---|
| ❑ | Tightspaces/ overhangs | Participant accidentally impacts head on overhang while walking/describing section, sustains laceration or superficial hematoma | - Safety and personal awareness<br>- Proper PPE (hard hat for overhangs and loose rock areas)<br>- First Aid training<br>- Awareness of hazards<br>- Selection of areas to be worked |
| ❑ | Foul weather | Weather suddenly changes, participant is scrambling to leave outcrop, slips, falls, and sustains injury | - Safety and personal awareness<br>- Go/No-Go criteria<br>- Emergency Response Plan<br>- Time of year<br>- Weather watch, awareness of forecast<br>- Lightning detector<br>- Weather radio<br>- Selection of alternate sites appropriate to be worked under unsettled weather conditions |
| ❑ | Animals—envenomation (North America) *[Foreign field work needs to be assessed separately]* | Participant sustains venomous bite, sting, or localized allergic reactions | - Safety and personal awareness<br>- First Aid training<br>- Proper PPE (gloves, footwear)<br>- Pre-trip medical screening for dangerous allergies, bring special medications as needed.<br>- First Aid kit<br>- Snakebite kit if appropriate<br>- Awareness of animal habitats and habits<br>- Emergency communications equipment<br>- Emergency Response Plan |
| ❑ | Animals—large carnivore *(N. America)* | Participant attacked by bear, cougar, or other large animal | - Safety and personal awareness<br>- Awareness of animal habitats and habits<br>- Anti-animal warning or defense devices<br>- Contract bear watch as appropriate<br>- Always work in groups<br>- Emergency communications equipment<br>- Emergency Response Plan |
| ❑ | Water/currents | Participant working near water, loses footing or swept into water by wave, and drowns | - Safety and personal awareness<br>- Proper PPE (footwear)<br>- Timing of visit to intertidal outcrops<br>- Training (example "Red Cross Community Water Safety")<br>- Hiking stick<br>- Loosen backpack straps and waist belt near water<br>- Selection of route/outcrops<br>- Rescue throw bag<br>- Consider use of PFD if most of time spent near water<br>- Awareness of water conditions (waves, tides, level)<br>- Emergency Response Plan |

## *Field Activity Safety Manual* 3R

| | Hazard Area | Event | Prevention and Mitigation Measures to Implement |
|---|---|---|---|
| ❑ | Vehicular traffic—pedestrian | Participant hit by vehicle while working along road or railroad | - Safety and personal awareness<br>- Proper PPE (reflective traffic safety vests)<br>- Maintain safe distance from traffic<br>- Awareness of local traffic customs, laws, etc (left/right hand driving, etc.)<br>- Traffic control devices<br>- Safe parking spot<br>- Designate traffic lookout<br>- Time of day and week for working outcrops |
| ❑ | Local inhabitants | Participant accidentally shot by hunter | - Safety and personal awareness<br>- Proper PPE (orange clothing in hunting areas)<br>- Avoid hunting season for field work<br>- Obtain permits for land access<br>- Awareness of local customs and inhabitants<br>- Emergency Response Plan |
| ❑ | Lifting and carrying | Participant injures back while lifting load that is too heavy or improperly lifted | - Safety and personal awareness<br>- Safe lifting techniques<br>- Proper conditioning<br>- Medical screening information<br>- Adequate personnel for lifting tasks |
| ❑ | Digging/ trenching | Trench collapses and injures participant (especially in soft sediments) | - Safety and personal awareness<br>- Proper PPE (gloves, eye protection)<br>- No trenches deeper than waist height<br>- Always have clear escape route<br>- Emergency Response Plan |
| ❑ | Use of hand tools | Tool slips and strikes participant or co-worker causing injury | - Safety and personal awareness<br>- Proper PPE (eye protection, gloves)<br>- Training in use of tool<br>- Frequent inspection of tools<br>- Hand guards on chisels, etc.<br>- Awareness of location of others<br>- Maintain safe area around person using tool<br>- Change out workers to avoid fatigue |
| ❑ | Equipment failure (power tools) | Participant struck by piece of faulty equipment or by rock fragment | - Safety and personal awareness<br>- Proper PPE (eye protection, gloves, other depending on equipment)<br>- Training in use of tool<br>- Frequent inspection of tools<br>- Awareness of location of others<br>- Maintain safe area around person using tool<br>- Change out workers to avoid fatigue |

## *Field Activity Safety Manual* *3R*

| | Hazard Area | Event | Prevention and Mitigation Measures to Implement |
|---|---|---|---|
| ❑ | Remote area (medical/ communication) | Consequence of injury escalates because of remoteness | - Safety and personal awareness<br>- Emergency Response Plan<br>- First Aid training<br>- Communications equipment<br>- Maps and GPS for efficient route selection<br>- First Aid kit<br>- Group interactions and assessments<br>- Adequate survival supplies<br>- Medical screening |
| ❑ | Water-borne and food-borne illnesses | Participant contracts illness from contaminated water or food | - Wash hands thoroughly and frequently<br>- Use packaged wipes for washing hands<br>- Drink only bottled water or other drinks<br>- Be sure food has been properly prepared and stored, not in direct contact with ice<br>- Do not drink melted water from ice chest or use ice from an ice chest in drinks<br>- Have anti-diarrhea medications and antibiotics in personal medical kit |
| ❑ | All other hazards | - Darkness/low light<br>- Strong sunlight<br>- Fire hazard<br>- Smoke/dust/fog<br>- Allergens<br>- Bridges/fences/utility lines<br>- Fatigue/dehydration<br>- Food handling<br>- Language/cultural differences<br>- Pre-existing Physical/medical needs<br>- Separation of individuals from group<br>- Lack of rest stops<br>- Individual behaviors/risk acceptance | - Standard operating procedures<br>- Standard personal protective equipment |

## In Water Activities

| | Hazard Area | Event | Prevention and Mitigation Measures to Implement |
|---|---|---|---|
| ❑ | Extreme water temperatures | Participant remains in cold water to long and develops hypothermia | - Safety and personal awareness to include hypothermia prevention and recognition.<br>- Proper PPE (recommend wearing wetsuit, "skin," or long-sleeved T-shirt while in water)<br>- First Aid training<br>- Strongly recommend eating good meal prior to prolonged exposure to the water<br>- Limit time in the water<br>- Swim in teams (buddy system) |

## *Field Activity Safety Manual* 3R

| | Hazard Area | Event | Prevention and Mitigation Measures to Implement |
|---|---|---|---|
| ❑ | Sharp objects, toxic or allergic sources such as:<br><br>*Marine water*—reef organisms, rocks<br><br>*Fresh water*—submerged tree limbs, rocks | Participant strikes or is struck by a sharp object in water resulting in a sting, cut, or blunt trauma | - Safety and personal awareness about marine life and their defense mechanisms including sharp, hard surfaces and chemical toxins<br>- Proper PPE (long-sleeved and long-legged swimwear, gloves)<br>- Self identify for allergic reactions; record information on personal medical form, make leaders aware of allergy<br>- Swim in teams (buddy system)<br>- First Aid kits on board<br>- Orientation to local conditions<br>- Emergency Response Plan |
| ❑ | Strong sunlight | Participant is exposed all day to direct sun and does not appropriately apply sunscreen cream, thus developing sunburn and possibly sun poisoning | - Safety and personal awareness about excessive sun exposure<br>- Use of PPE including recommended head gear and long-sleeved/legged clothing<br>- First aid kit and training<br>- Extra sunscreen with activity coordinator |
| ❑ | Toxic/allergic sources<br><br>• Marine waters defense toxins<br>• Fresh waters Bacteria, toxins | Participant comes in contact with a toxic source or an allergen resulting in paralysis or an extreme allergic reaction | - Safety and personal awareness<br>- Use of PPE including recommended head gear and long-sleeved/legged clothing<br>- First Aid training<br>- First Aid kit on board<br>- Emergency Response Plan |
| ❑ | Animals<br><br>• Marine waters: Barracuda Sharks<br>• Fresh water: Snakes, Alligators, Leeches | Participant comes in contact with an aggressive animal while in the water resulting in an attack, bite or string—the event causes excessive bleeding or shock | - Safety and personal awareness about swimming in open ocean and about large fish behavior; dangers of bleeding in ocean<br>- Safety and personal awareness about swimming in designated fresh water environment and what animals to be aware of in that environment.<br>- First aid CPR training<br>- Pre-trip swim/snorkel skills test<br>- Field activity team members act as spotters for one another while conducting in-water activities.<br>- PFD wear required<br>- Emergency Response Plan |

## *Field Activity Safety Manual* 3R

| | Hazard Area | Event | Prevention and Mitigation Measures to Implement |
|---|---|---|---|
| ❑ | Swimming, wading, and snorkeling, water (waves, tides, currents, depth) | Case 1. Participant takes in water through snorkel while swimming in high waves, panics, and submerges and drowns<br><br>Case 2. Participant is not familiar with swimming in deep water (>30 ft), panics, and submerges and drowns<br><br>Case 3. Participant is swept away in current or swiftness of river flow, and submerges and drowns | - Medical check for physical fitness before activity<br>- Pre-activity check for swimming ability, limit participation to appropriate level of swimming ability<br>- Examine swim area for hazards and depth<br>- Safety and personal awareness<br>- In water field activities monitored by members of the field activity party as lookout/lifeguard<br>- Self-identification for non-participation in any activity<br>- Strategic positioning of boats as boundary markers for snorkeling area<br>- Remain in area designated for in-water activities<br>- Required buddy system<br>- PFD wear required<br>- Emergency Response Plan |
| ❑ | Lifting/carrying | Participant is dragged under the water while trying to carry heavy equipment to shore resulting in water inhalation | - Safety and personal awareness<br>- First Aid training<br>- PFD wear required<br>- Emergency Response Plan |
| ❑ | Fatigue/ dehydration | Participant does not drink enough fluid throughout the day and expends more energy than normal while swimming, becomes tired and disoriented while in the water, panics, and submerges resulting in drowning | - Safety and personal awareness highlighting fatigue and dehydration<br>- First Aid training<br>- Field activity team will watch for signs of dehydration<br>- Required swim test<br>- Required PFD wear<br>- Required buddy system<br>- Coolers with sufficient drinks aboard each boat or on shore by work party<br>- Maximum 100 m distance from boats during all snorkel stops<br>- Scheduling of stops to preclude overexertion<br>- Emergency Response Plan |

## *Field Activity Safety Manual* 3R

| | Hazard Area | Event | Prevention and Mitigation Measures to Implement |
|---|---|---|---|
| ❑ | Language or cultural differences | Participant or buddy pair has English as second language, misunderstands instructions during daily safety and activities briefing, separates from group in water, becomes distressed, panics, submerges and drowns | - Safety and personal awareness<br>- First Aid training<br>- At least one strong English speaker in each pair<br>- Use communication techniques to verify understanding of safety and personal awareness<br>- Field activity coordinator make individual contact with non-native speakers to verify understanding<br>- Provide boundaries and out of bounds areas to all participants<br>- Required PFD wear<br>- Required buddy system<br>- Emergency Response Plan |
| ❑ | Pre-existing physical/ medical needs | Participant has pre-existing physical condition that is private medical information, participates in an in-water activity that exacerbates or re-activates the condition, becomes distressed, panics, and submerges and drowns | - Safety and personal awareness<br>- First Aid training<br>- Required medical release prior to admission to school<br>- Self-identification for exclusion from activity<br>- Pre-trip notification to field work coordinator regarding pre-existing conditions so that mitigation or special equipment can be secured to achieve safe execution of the activity<br>- Required PFD wear<br>- Buddy system<br>- Emergency Response Plan |
| ❑ | Separation of individuals from Group; Individual behaviors and risk acceptance | Participant or participants decide to venture away from group against instruction, or because of curiosity, trouble is encountered due to high-energy ocean conditions, heavy currents, distance from boats, or animal attack, then one or both is/are distressed, panic, submerge and drown | - Safety and personal awareness<br>- Field work coordinator monitors behavior of participants and make adjustments as required<br>- First Aid training<br>- Pre trip letter from management<br>- Required PFD wear<br>- Required buddy system<br>- Remain in area designated for in-water activities<br>- Emergency Response Plan |
| ❑ | Equipment failure | Case 1. Participant purchases inferior quality mask and snorkel, during swimming/snorkel stop, snorkel tube fails and person experiences temporary inability to breathe, panics, submerges and drowns<br><br>Case 2. Delegate punctures inflated PFD in deep water (>15 ft), becomes fatigued in return swim to boat, panics, submerges and drowns | - Safety and personal awareness<br>- First Aid training<br>- Pre-course instructions include recommendations for equipment standards<br>- Snorkel gear to be evaluated and approved by vendor during snorkel skills test<br>- Required PFD wear<br>- Required buddy system<br>- Lookout and Lifeguard in boats monitoring group<br>- Emergency Response Plan |

## *Field Activity Safety Manual* *3R*

| | Hazard Area | Event | Prevention and Mitigation Measures to Implement |
|---|---|---|---|
| ❑ | Limited or remote medical services | Participant sustains a non-life threatening injury; however, condition may worsen due to extended and strenuous transport to medical facility by boat | - Safety and personal awareness<br>- First Aid training<br>- Field first aid kit and backboard/restraint system onboard<br>- Shock prevention measures<br>- Satellite phone onboard<br>- Emergency Response Plan |
| ❑ | Limited communications | Participant sustains a non-life threatening injury however; there is not cell or satellite coverage in the area for Emergency response—the condition may worsen due to extended and strenuous transport to medical facility by boat | - Safety and personal awareness<br>- First Aid training<br>- Field first aid kit and backboard/restraint system onboard<br>- Shock prevention measures<br>- Satellite phone onboard<br>- Emergency Response Plan<br>- CPR training<br>- Ship to shore radios |
| ❑ | All other in-water activities | Minor accidents | - Safety and personal awareness<br>- First Aid training<br>- Emergency Response Plan |

*Field Activity Safety Manual* *3R*

# Personal Protective and Safety Equipment

| Action | Required PPE | Recommended PPE |
|---|---|---|
| **Hiking**—outcrops, trails, desert environment, loose rock. | ❑ Appropriate sturdy footwear (i.e. hiking boots with leather/puncture-resistant uppers and Vibram-type non-slip soles) | ❑ Long pants and long sleeve shirts<br>❑ Sun glasses<br>❑ Sun screen<br>❑ Wide-brimmed hat<br>❑ Water canteen<br>❑ Hiking stick<br>❑ Insect repellent<br>❑ Emergency whistle<br>❑ Two-way communications |
| **Roadside activities**—outcrop road-cuts, access to outcrops. | ❑ Safety vest (high-visibility color)<br>❑ Traffic warning markers | ❑ Personal safety warning light |
| **Sampling with rock hammers** (chipping)—outcrops, hand specimens | ❑ Safety glasses | ❑ Leather gloves |
| **Sampling with trenching tools** (digging)—slopes, pits, outcrops | ❑ Safety glasses<br>❑ Leather gloves | ❑ Steel-toed work boots |
| **Activities in mouth of caves or under overhangs**—outcrops, sampling | ❑ Hard hats<br>❑ Safety glasses | ❑ Headlamp |
| **Boating** | ❑ Life vest (PFD of appropriate type, typically Type II or III),<br>❑ Footwear with non-skid soles appropriate for boating | ❑ Sun screen<br>❑ Sun glasses<br>❑ Water canteen<br>❑ Wide-brimmed hat |
| **Cold weather activities**—arctic sampling, outcrops | ❑ Thermal footwear, headwear, and outerwear<br>❑ Gloves<br>❑ Safety glasses<br>❑ Two-way communication | ❑ Waterproof footwear<br>❑ Thermal underwear<br>❑ Hand warmers |
| **Other activity:** | ❑<br>❑<br>❑<br>❑ | |

## Field Activity Safety Process 3S

# Field Activity Risk Assessment - Potential Hazards Register

*Include notes on local conditions:*

*What is the probability of: 1. an occurrence with serious consequences (levels I, II, or III), or 2. many/frequent incidents with level IV consequences during a single session or site visit?*

*Notes on local issues, important safeguards to use, and scenarios to be assessed*

| Potential Hazard | Probability of Occurrence H | M | L | NA | Comments Issues-Mitigators-Scenarios |
|---|---|---|---|---|---|
| **Natural Environment** — *Criteria, Limits, Critical Factors to consider:* | | | | | |
| Temperature Extremes (Hot/Cold) ≅ *Temperature (> 30°C, < 5°C), Wind, Humidity* | | | | | *Length of Exposure , Time of Year/Day* |
| Uneven/Slippery Walking Surfaces ≅ *Slip, trip, or fall that results in injury* | | | | | *Cumulative Fatigue, Weather* |
| Sharp Objects–rocks, coral, vegetation ≅ *Contact or fall results in penetrating wound/scratched cornea* | | | | | *Visibility, Fatigue, Exact Route* |
| Heights/Drop-offs (inc. high elevation) ≅ *Fall that results in free-fall drop of more than 2 m* | | | | | *Slope/softness of "landing" zone* |
| Falling Objects/Obstructions ≅ *Spontaneous/Participant-caused, capable of causing serious injury* | | | | | *Time of year, freshness of outcrop* |
| Tight Spaces/Narrow Openings/Overhangs ≅ *Results in impact or crushing injury, or panic/distress* | | | | | *Visibility, crowding,* |
| Darkness/Low Light ≅ *Contributing factor to other hazards that result in injury* | | | | | *Visibility, Fatigue, Weather* |
| Strong Sunlight (inc. sunburn) ≅ *Serious sunburn, "snow" blindness, contributing factor to fatigue* | | | | | *Exposure length, surface albedo* |
| Foul Weather Considerations– wind, rain, snow, lightning, flash flood ≅ *Local, upstream* | | | | | *Before and During activity* |
| Fire Hazard ≅ *Hot vehicle exhaust system/discarded cigarette causes fire, traps group, endangers ecosystem* | | | | | *Access to site during fire bans* |
| Smoke/Dust/Fog ≅ *Causes eye/throat/nose injury, contributing factor to other hazards* | | | | | *Time of year/day* |
| Toxic/Allergic Sources(vegetation, pollen) ≅ *Causes acute reaction, contributing factor to other hazards* | | | | | *Time of year, EMS access* |
| Animals—Insects, Reptiles, Mammals, Other ≅ *Causes trauma, envenomation, allergic reaction* | | | | | *Time of year, local experience* |
| Water/Current ≅ *Fall results in submersion, Strenuous exertion in water triggers pre-existing medical condition* | | | | | *Time of day/year, Hypothermia* |
| **Man-Made Environment (for Pedestrians)** | | | | | |
| Vehicular Traffic—Roads, Railroads ≅ *Vehicle impacts participant, Group activity causes traffic hazard* | | | | | *Time of day/year* |
| Bridges ≅ *Vehicle impacts participant, Group activity causes traffic hazard* | | | | | *Sidewalk, width of shoulder* |
| Fences ≅ *If gate not available, crossing results in fall, impact, lacerations, penetrating wound* | | | | | *Property owner interactions* |
| Utility Lines ≅ *Approach route or portions of outcrop allow contact with power lines, resulting in injury* | | | | | *Alternate routes* |
| Local Inhabitants (inc. hunters) ≅ *Group provokes hazardous reaction from locals; distraction factor* | | | | | *Time of year/day* |
| Crowds/Spectators ≅ *Group provokes hazardous reaction from locals; distraction factor* | | | | | *Time of year/day* |
| **Transportation (Auto, Boat, Air)** | | | | | |
| Vehicle Condition ≅ *Primary or contributing factor to accident/collision* | | | | | *Rental company, local experience* |
| Driver Qualification/Experience for location ≅ *Primary or contributing factor to accident/collision* | | | | | *Availability of local drivers* |
| Route Conditions—rough (inc. flat tires) ≅ *Rough enough to be contributing factor to accident/collision* | | | | | *Type of vehicle used, local drivers* |
| Route Conditions—congestion ≅ *Enough to be contributing factor to accident, esp. around airport and major cities* | | | | | *Time of day, Route selection* |
| Route Conditions—winding, limited sight line ≅ *Enough to be contributing factor to accident/collision* | | | | | *Time of day, Route selection* |
| Pedestrians ≅ *Sufficiently numerous or common to be contributing factor to accident* | | | | | *Time of day, Route selection* |
| Intersections/Railroad Crossings ≅ *Hazardous/Unguarded/Confusing location contributes to accident* | | | | | *Time of day, Route selection* |
| **Human Factors/Participant Activities** | | | | | |
| Hiking/Walking ≅ *Intensity, length, duration, cumulative exertion sufficient to trigger illness, contribute to injury* | | | | | *Time of day/year, Weather* |
| Climbing ≅ *Requires use of both hands to ascend/descend more than 2 m vertical, exposure to fall and injury* | | | | | *Weather, outcrop condition* |
| Lifting/Carrying ≅ *Improper technique/overloaded backpacks results in injury* | | | | | *Gear selection, individual fitness* |
| Swimming/Snorkeling/SCUBA/Boating ≅ *Improper technique/conditioning/equipment causes injury* | | | | | *Pre-trip screening, PFD policy* |
| Digging/Trenching ≅ *Digging causes injury to self or other participant, Trench collapse causes injury* | | | | | *OSHA rules for deep trenches* |
| Use of Tools (inc. chipping) ≅ *Improper technique/equipment causes injury to self or other participant* | | | | | *Required PPE* |
| Extended Immobility ≅ *Enough to be contributing factor to accident, trigger pre-existing medical condition* | | | | | *Agenda/Travel planning* |
| Fatigue/Dehydration ≅ *Enough to be contributing factor to accident, trigger pre-existing medical condition* | | | | | *Agenda, Time of year/day* |
| Food Handling ≅ *Improper technique/equipment contributes to food-borne illness* | | | | | *Training, Sanitation facilities* |
| Language/Culture Differences ≅ *Contributing factor to accident* | | | | | *Pre-trip participant information* |
| Pre-Existing Physical/Medical Needs ≅ *Contributing factor to accident, acute episode of illness* | | | | | *Pre-trip participant information* |
| Separation of Individuals from Group ≅ *Contributing factor to accident* | | | | | *Safety briefings, Read backs* |
| Lack of Rest Stops/Facilities ≅ *Contributing factor to fatigue, accident* | | | | | *Pre-trip planning* |
| Individual Behaviors/Risk Acceptance ≅ *Contributing factor to accident* | | | | | *Management letter, briefings* |
| Equipment Failure ≅ *Sufficiently critical and serious to be contributing factor to accident* | | | | | *Pre-trip planning, inspections* |
| **Other Factors** | | | | | |
| Limited/Remote Medical Services ≅ *Consequence of injury/illness escalates due to remoteness* | | | | | *Pre-trip plan, communications* |
| Limited Communications ≅ *Consequence of injury/illness escalates due to delayed access to EMS assistance* | | | | | *Pre-trip planning, field checks* |
| *Additional Hazards identified by team?* ≅ *Significantly different, likely to have serious consequences* | | | | | *Consult local experts, experience* |

## Field Activity Safety Process 3S1

# Field Activity Risk Assessment - Potential Hazards Register

Field Activity: ______________________ Dates: ______________

Site Name: ______________________

| Potential Hazard | Probability of Occurrence | | | | Comments Issues-Mitigators-Scenarios |
|---|---|---|---|---|---|
| | H | M | L | NA | |
| **Natural Environment** | | | | | |
| Temperature Extremes (Hot/Cold) | | | | | |
| Uneven/Slippery WalkingSurfaces | | | | | |
| Sharp Objects—rocks, coral, vegetation | | | | | |
| Heights/Drop-offs (inc. high elevation) | | | | | |
| Falling Objects/Obstructions | | | | | |
| Tight Spaces/Narrow Openings/Overhangs | | | | | |
| Darkness/Low Light | | | | | |
| Strong Sunlight (including sunburn) | | | | | |
| Foul Weather—wind, rain, snow, lightning, flash flood | | | | | |
| Fire Hazard | | | | | |
| Smoke/Dust/Fog | | | | | |
| Toxic/Allergic Sources (vegetation, pollen) | | | | | |
| Animals—Insects, Reptiles, Mammals, Other | | | | | |
| Water/Current—streams, waves, tides, depth | | | | | |
| **Man-Made Environment (for Pedestrians)** | | | | | |
| Vehicular Traffic—Roads, Railroads | | | | | |
| Bridges | | | | | |
| Fences | | | | | |
| Utility Lines | | | | | |
| Local Inhabitants (inc. hunters) | | | | | |
| Crowds/Spectators | | | | | |
| **Transportation (Auto, Boat, Air)** | | | | | |
| Vehicle Condition *(safety equipment, mechanical, tires, etc.)* | | | | | |
| Driver Qualification/Experience for location | | | | | |
| Route Conditions—rough (inc. flat tires) | | | | | |
| Route Conditions—congestion | | | | | |
| Route Conditions—winding, limited sight line | | | | | |
| Pedestrians | | | | | |
| Intersections/Railroad Crossings | | | | | |
| **Human Factors / Participant Activities** | | | | | |
| Hiking/Walking | | | | | |
| Climbing | | | | | |
| Lifting/Carrying | | | | | |
| Swimming/Snorkeling/SCUBA/Boating | | | | | |
| Digging/Trenching | | | | | |
| Use of Tools (including chipping) | | | | | |
| Extended Immobility (auto, boat, air) | | | | | |
| Fatigue/Dehydration | | | | | |
| Food Handling | | | | | |
| Language/Culture Differences | | | | | |
| Pre-Existing Physical/Medical Needs | | | | | |
| Separation of Individuals from Group | | | | | |
| Lack of Rest Stops/Facilities | | | | | |
| Individual Behaviors Risk Acceptance | | | | | |
| Equipment Failure | | | | | |
| **Other Factors** | | | | | |
| Limited/Remote Medical Services | | | | | |
| Limited Communications | | | | | |
| *Additional Hazards identified by team?* | | | | | |

# Field Activity Safety Process 3T

## Emergency Medical Information

Emergency Medical Information
ATTENTION

In an emergency when I am unable to communicate or am unconscious, please use the information on this card to provide appropriate care.

*Personal Identification:*

Name: ____________________

Address: ____________________

____________________

____________________

Phone:

*Notify in an Emergency:*

Name: ____________________

Address: ____________________

____________________

Phone: ____________________

Name: ____________________

Address: ____________________

____________________

Phone ____________________

My Doctor: ____________________

Address: ____________________

____________________

Phone: ____________________

Religion: ____________________

Medical Information: Date:

Present Medical Conditions: ____________________

____________________

____________________

Medications Taken Regularly: ____________________

____________________

____________________

Dangerous Allergies: ____________________

____________________

____________________

Other Important Information: ____________________

____________________

____________________

Blood Type: ____________________

Global Medical Response telephone (USA)
123-456-7890

This global number provides access to the following types of assi stance, as dictated by circumstances:

- 24-hour telephone medical advice
- Access to a local preferred medical provider
- Medical Evacuation
- Contact with the Organization physician-on-call

*To be completed and carried on your person during field trip (will fit in passport when folded in half)*

# 4 Pre-Activity Safety Review

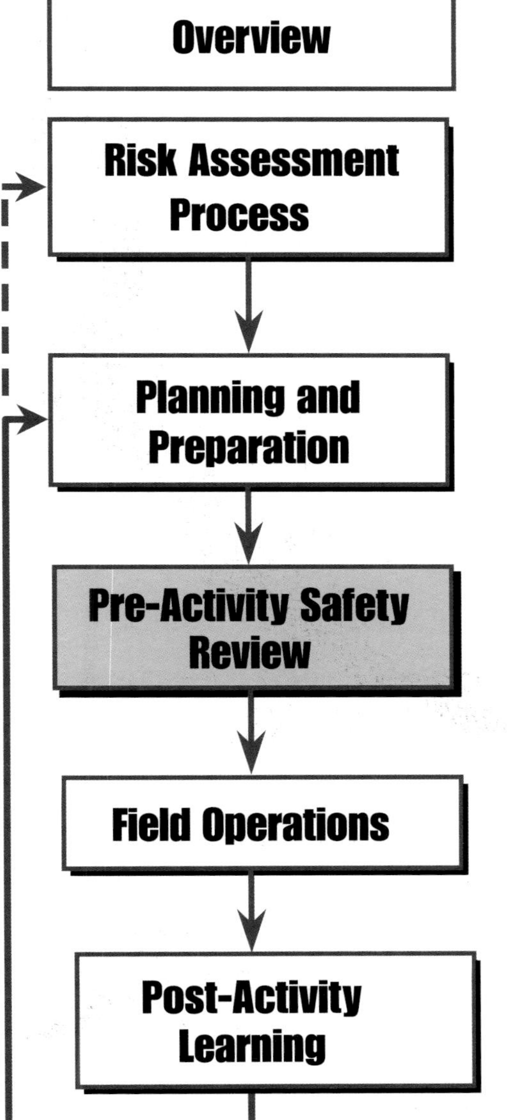

*"At last, everything was in readiness. The hour had arrived towards which the persevering labor of years had been incessantly bent, and with it the feeling that, everything having been provided and completed, responsibility might be thrown aside and the weary brain at last find rest."*

*Fridtjof Nansen, 1897, Farthest North*

# SECTION 4

## Pre-Activity Safety Review

All Field Activities must be approved by the Activity Owner prior to being conducted. This approval is usually obtained at the conclusion of a Pre-Activity Safety Review meeting in which the Activity Coordinator presents the preparations and plans for the Activity. The meeting typically lasts about 30 minutes if all of the Field Activity documentation is completed properly. The meeting is to be scheduled by the Activity Coordinator. Approval must be secured a minimum of 2 weeks prior to the scheduled start of Field Schools or Field Trips, and 1 week prior to Fieldwork. The cover page of the Field Activity SHE Plan, entitled ***Activity Preparation Approval*** form is provided to document the preparations and approval.

The attendees of the Review meeting are:

- Activity Coordinator or designee (required)
- Appropriate SHE representative (required)
- Activity Owner or designee (required)
- Field Safety Coordinator (optional)
- Other Activity Staff (optional)

### Agenda

Using the cover sheet of the Field Activity SHE plan as a guide, discuss:

- Any conditions affecting the current Risk Assessment or the new Risk Assessment constructed for this activity
- Special needs of participants as requested on the Safety Acknowledgments or Medical Release forms and planned accomodations or delivery plan changes
- Field Activity SHE and ERP documents
- Special travel arrangements (as applicable)
- Any waiver or other special situations

### Supporting Documentation

Along with the ***Field Activity SHE Plan*** with attached ***Risk Assessment Summary Report*** and ***Emergency Response Plan***, the following supporting documentation should be available:

- Site Summary Sheets (attachments to the ERP)
- Completed Potential Hazard Register forms for each site (as used in the risk assessment)
- Safety Watch Pack contents list
- All Participant Safety Acknowledgement forms (completed)
- Participant roster
- Activity Guidebook (for Schools and Trips)
- Any other documents and materials that were used in the preparation of the Activity:
  - ☐ ***Activity Agenda***
  - ☐ ***Foreign Travel Approval Form***—when applicable (organization specific)
  - ☐ ***Travel Warrant or other travel procedure Form***—when applicable (organization specific)
  - ☐ ***Non-scheduled Aircraft Approval Form***—when applicable (organization specific)
  - ☐ ***Waiver Approval Form*** (Training or Staff: Participant ratio)


DOI:10.1306/1119800DEG3223

# 5 Field Operations

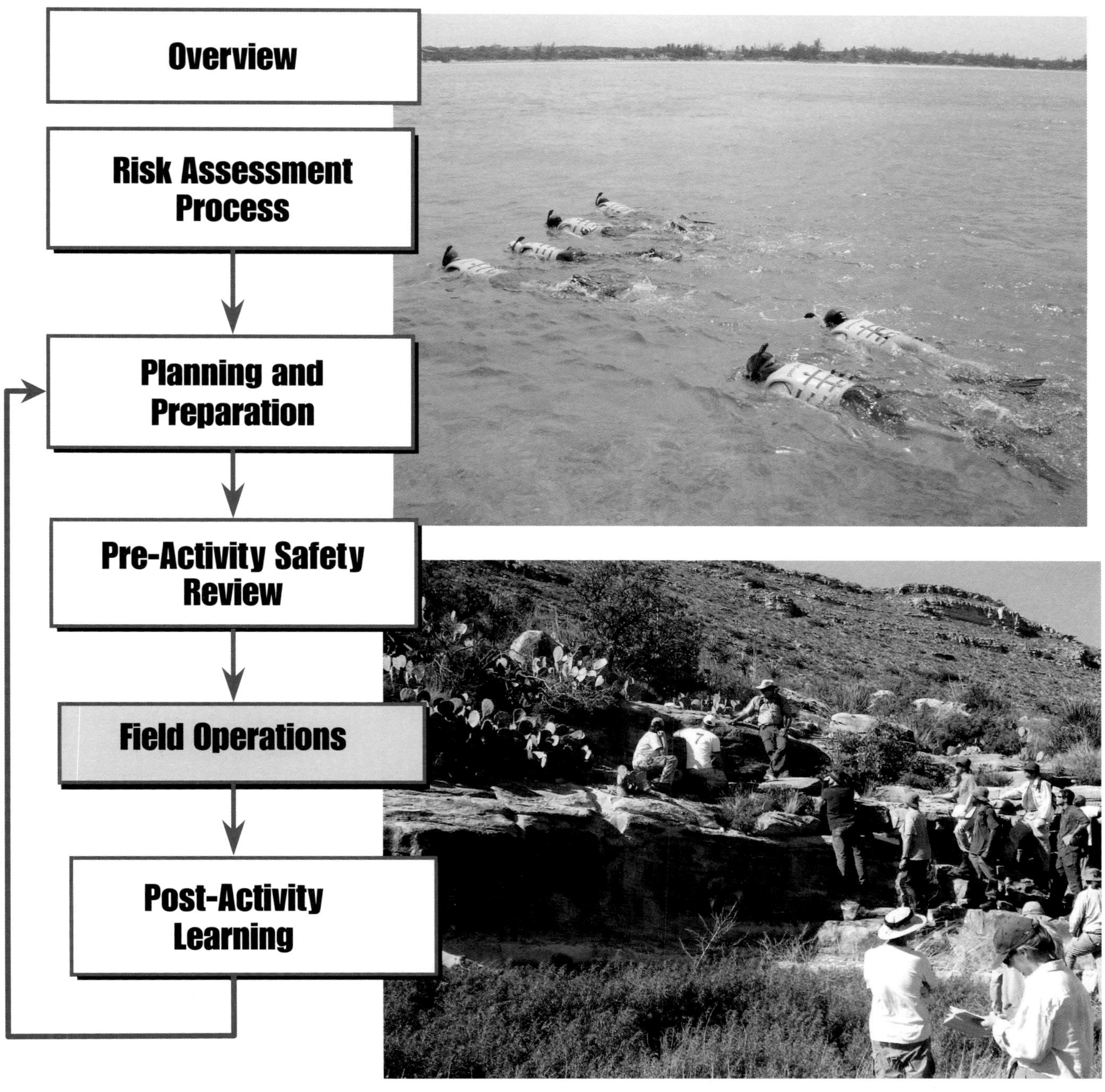

*"One who goes gently goes safely, one who goes safely, goes far."*

*Mocoa, Darién native, Colombia, 1927*

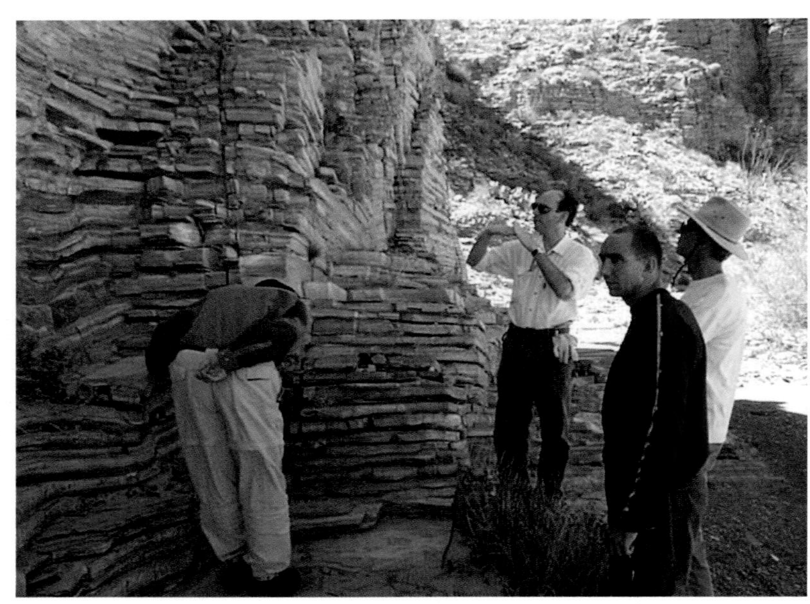

# SECTION 5

## Field Operations

The following **In-Field Safety Procedures** section defines in detail the safety-related process and requirements for Field Activities. Whenever possible, these procedures should be integrated with the delivery of the technical message for increased effectiveness.

The following document describes various safety-related activities that occur **during** a field activity in chronological order from the start of a school/trip/work to closing. These key procedures and products include:

- Assembling a Field Safety Resource Book
  - PPE, Activity Safety Equipment Check Out
  - Pre-Activity Field Checks
  - Initial Safety Orientation:
    - Introduction and General Briefing
    - Assign Drivers
    - Assign Groups or Buddy Pairs and Roles
    - Brief Drivers as a Sub Group
    - Check everyone's required PPE (especially footwear and eye protection)
    - Issue SHE and Communications Equipment to each group
  - Daily Morning Safety Briefings
  - Site Safety Briefing:
    - Use of barriers and warning devices
    - Field Safety Log Book
  - Standard Operating Procedures (SOPs)
    - Pre-trip Water Safety Class Requirements
    - Road Walking Exposure
    - Insert
  - Change Management during Activity
  - Daily Safety Debriefings
  - End of Activity Debriefing

**The following forms for this section are also located on the CD-Rom accompanying this book:**
**Field Safety Orientation Slide Template—5A**
**Safety Log Book Outline and Example Entries—5B**
**Participant Safety Card Template—5C**

### IN-FIELD SAFETY PROCEDURES

#### Overview

This document describes the various safety-related activities that occur **during** a field activity from the start of a school/trip/work to closing. Where possible, these activities should be integrated into other activities (e.g. initial orientation, school/trip critiques, etc.).

#### Field Safety Resource Book:

A Field Safety Resource Book will be assembled for each activity and a copy issued to each vehicle. This Manual will contain:

- School/Trip Agenda
- Drivers Safety Briefing Sheet
- Emergency Response Plan
- Site Summary Sheets
- SHE Plan
- Other Items and Maps as appropriate

#### PPE, Safety Equipment Check Out

Logistics Coordinator and Safety Watch, prior to leaving for the field, should check out phones, barriers, vehicle safety kits, etc., along with school Safety and personal PPE such as boots, safety glasses, and gloves. Required PPE is specified in the SHE Plan.

#### Pre-Activity Field Checks

The Activity Staff is encouraged to check local conditions prior to the scheduled start of the Activity to review the conditions of roads and confirm access routes, review potential hazards, etc. In some cases it may be necessary for two of the activity staff to visit key sites just prior to the activity to verify conditions.


DOI:10.1306/1119801DEG3223

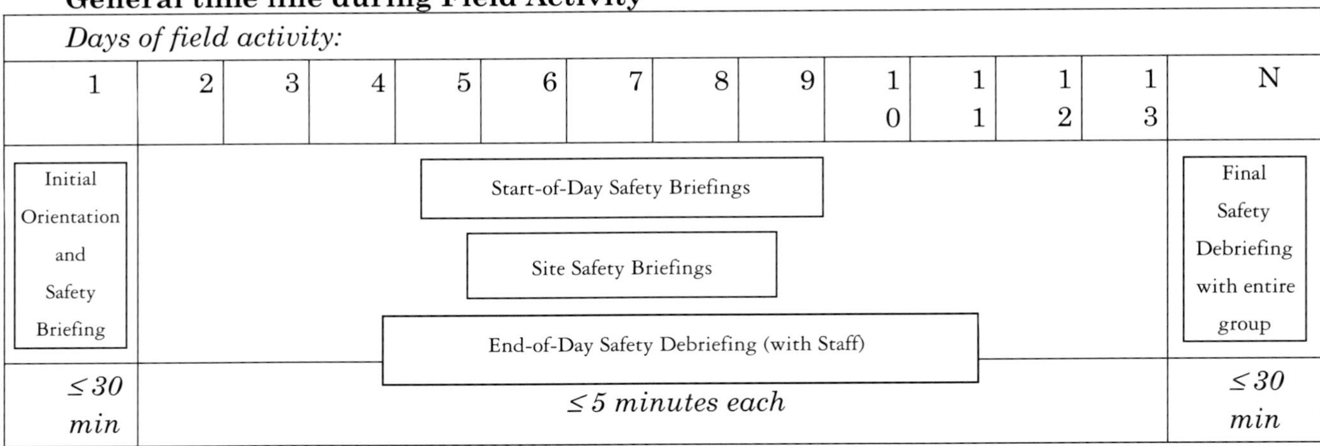

General time line during Field Activity
Days of field activity:
1
2
3
4
5
6
7
8
9
10
11
12
13
N
Initial Orientation and Safety Briefing
Start-of-Day Safety Briefings
Site Safety Briefings
End-of-Day Safety Debriefing (with Staff)
Final Safety Debriefing with entire group
≤30 min
≤5 minutes each
≤30 min


## Initial Safety Orientation

This safety orientation is part of the initial orientation conducted the first morning (or sometimes the first evening) of the activity. It is intended to communicate to the participants the general safety principles and requirements. Specific stop hazards, precautions, etc., will be covered in daily and stop safety briefings. Detailed information for drivers is discussed with the smaller group of persons actually driving. The whole briefing system is designed to provide detailed safety information just in time. This Initial Orientation will be conducted by the school/trip/work coordinator/instructor and/or Safety Watch.

The general order of operations is:

- Introduction and General Briefing
- Assign Drivers
- Assign Groups or Buddy Pairs and Roles
- Brief Drivers as a sub group
- Check everyone's required PPE (especially footwear and eye protection)
- Issue SHE and Communications Equipment to each group

### Introduction and General Briefing:

Contents of the General Safety Briefing include:

- Overview, Safety Philosophy, Expectations
- Roles, Responsibilities of Safety Watch, Instructors, Logistics Coordinator, and participants
- Resources (cards, manuals, vehicle notebooks, etc.)
- General Procedures
  - Participation (what to do if you are not comfortable performing a task)
  - Whistles, emergencies
  - Radios
  - Convoys
  - Groups
  - Illness, injuries, near misses, hazard reporting
  - PPE (boots, clothing, sunscreen, hats, etc.)
  - Management of Change
- Driving (Key Points only)
  - Alcohol use and transportation prohibited
  - Use of vehicle by other people than designated driver
  - Procedure if a person is not comfortable with driver
- Risk Perception
- Emergency Response
  - ERPs
  - Roles, responsibilities
- Participant Issues, Questions, Quiz/Discussion

A standard template of slides for this orientation is available from the Geoscience Field Safety Coordinator (see form 5A, above).

## Assign Groups and Roles

- ▸ At the end of the initial safety briefing, the Activity Staff will make Group/Buddy assignments based on participants' skills, experience, culture, interests, etc., before the first field stop.
- ▸ Specific staff roles and responsibilities such as Safety Watch will be assigned the first day of the activity or before. The Safety Watch's primary

*(text is continued on page 140)*

5A
Your Organization

## Your School

- Welcome, Classroom Safety, Introductions
- Technical Overview
- Safety Overview
- Logistics Overview
- Q & A...
- Safety Scenarios

5A
Your Organization

## Your School

- Welcome
- Classroom Safety:
  - Fire Exits, Assembly Point
- Introductions
  - Staff and roles
  - Participants and experience

5A
Your Organization

*Your School*

- **Technical Overview:**
  - **Learning Objectives:**
    - ...
    - ...
    - ...
  - **Learning Activities:**
    - **Lectures**
    - **Classroom Exercises: Seismic, Well Logs**
    - **Outcrop Exercises: Description, Correlation, Tracing**

5A
Your Organization

*Your School*

- **Safety Overview:**
  - **Safety is and must be everyone's goal and responsibility**
  - **Safe operations enhance your learning experience**
  - **Hazards have been carefully evaluated and mitigation processes are in place:**
    - **Field Safety Team**
    - **Standard Operations Plans**
    - **Emergency Response Plan**
    - **School and Participant Resources**
  - **YOUR Attitude and Awareness are most important!**

5A
Your Organization

## Your School: Standard Field Ops

- **Lead Instructor:**
  - **Coordinates overall activity, safety, and emergency action**
  - **Stays out in front of all groups during movements**
- **Safety Watch**
  - **Maintains safety watch, enforces safety rules, keeps log**
  - **Carries outcrop safety and response equipment**
  - **Stays at rear of group during movements ("sweep")**
- **Assistant Instructor**
  - **Assists with technical training and safe conduct**
  - **Stays in the middle of the class during movements**
- **Logistics Coordinator**
  - **Assists with safe conduct and general health of class**
  - **Issues safety equipment**
  - **Safety watch for those in parking area**

Safety Watch
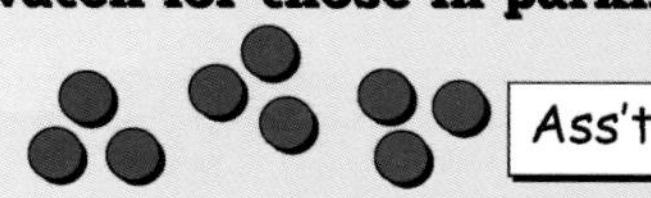
Ass't

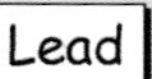
Lead

5A
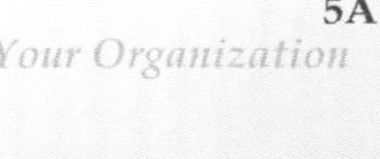
Your Organization

## Your School: Standard Field Ops

- **Work Groups—YOU!**
  - **Watch out for each other**
  - **Detect Problems Early**
  - **Alert school to problems quickly**
  - **Make Initial Response to injury/illness**
    - **Remain with injured/ill person**
    - **Prevent further harm**
    - **DO NOT MOVE injured unless in immediate danger**
    - **Identify urgent issues:**
      - **Breathing**
      - **Pulse**
      - **Severe Bleeding**

Safety Watch
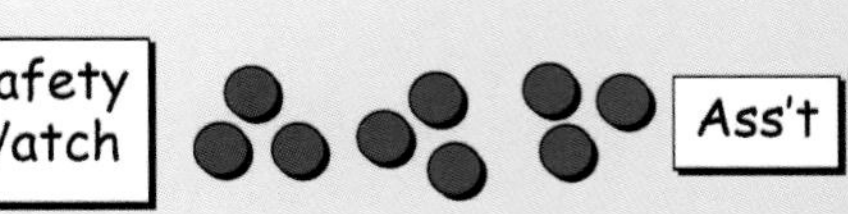
Ass't
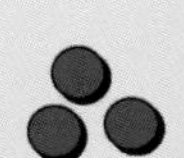
Lead

5A
Your Organization

## Your School: Emergency Response

- **Lead Instructor:**
  - **Coordinates overall response**
- **Safety Watch**
  - **Provides initial First Aid**
- **Assistant Instructor**
  - **Assists with technical training and safe conduct**
  - **Stays in the middle of the class during movements**
- **Logistics Coordinator**
  - **Assists with uninvolved groups**
  - **Assists with emergency notification**

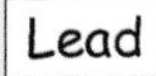


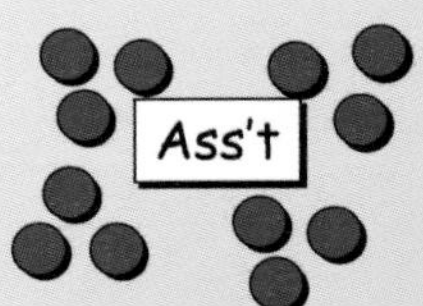


5A
Your Organization

## Your School

- **Safety Overview:**
  - **Safety is and must be everyone's goal and responsibility**
  - **Safe Operations Enhance your learning experience**
  - **Hazards have been carefully evaluated and mitigation processes are in place:**
    - **YOUR Attitude and Awareness are most important!**
    - **Field Safety Team**
    - **Standard Operations Plans**
    - **Emergency Response Plan**
    - **School and Participant Resources**
  - **Field Ops, Roles and Responsibilities: Normal, Emergency**
  - **Resources (hand out to participants)**

5A
Your Organization

## Your School

- If you are not comfortable participating in any activity for any reason, you are encouraged to notify the Coordinator or other Staff member. There are no negative implications for this decision.
- If you become uncomfortable with the actions or behavior of your fellow participants, please notify one of the School Staff or the Field Safety Coordinator. Your concerns will be kept confidential and actions will be taken to remedy the situation.
- If you become uncomfortable with the actions or behavior of one of the Staff members, please contact the Field Safety Coordinator at the earliest convenient time. Your concerns will be kept confidential and actions will be taken to remedy the situation.
- The Field Safety Coordinator, NAME??, can be reached at 1-123-456-7890??, or by email: GFSC@null.net??

5A
Your Organization

## Your School

- **Logistics Overview:**
  - **Boot Check...**
  - **Vehicles (including driver responsibilities)**
  - **Flights**
  - **Lodging**

5A
Your Organization

Your School

- Q & A…
- Safety Scenarios

5A
Your Organization

Scenario 1 & 2:

- Normal safe operation
  - How do we identify hazards?
  - What keeps us from getting hurt?
- Emergency response:
  - At a particular site, somebody gets hurt
  - What are the Group actions?
  - Who provides first aid?
  - Who calls for help?
  - What do the uninvolved participants do?

## Field Activity Safety Process 5B

# Daily Entries in Safety Log Book

The Safety Watch is responsible for making daily entries in the "Safety Log" book. Entries should include:

- All safety or health concerns, feedback, and suggestions identified by field trip participants.
- All Unsafe Acts, Hazards or Unsafe Conditions, and Safety Observations identified by the Staff or Participants.
- A summary of Incidents, Near Misses, and First Aid treatment that occurred during the day.

The purpose of making these log entries is to allow for all Leading and Lagging Indicators to be identified, in order to provide input for future safety and health improvements in the Field Activities as well as the processes and protocols for Field Activities.

By the beginning of the next day, the Safety Log entries will be reviewed with the Activity Coordinator and all appropriate information communicated to the Participants.

An explanation of the typical daily entry of information is as follows:

1. Date of Log Entry
2. Name of Safety Watch or individual making entry
3. Number of Staff and Participants (to help provide an estimate of exposure hours.)
4. Name of the Activity being conducted
5. General location of day's activities
6. Specific location where a hazard, unsafe condition, safety observation, near miss, or incident was encountered.
7. Listing of Participant-identified Safety Concerns or Feedback.
   Examples:
   - Not enough water available for all participants for the hike in the afternoon.
   - Food for lunch was not kept cool and appeared to have spoiled when it was left in the vehicle during our hot morning hike.
   - The hotel fire exits were not properly marked on the second floor.
8. Listing of Hazards or Unsafe Conditions, and Safety Observations encountered
   Examples:
   - On the second stop there was a difficult and narrow hiking surface with loose gravel and loose rocks. This made it hard to walk without periodically tripping.
   - A stream crossing was encountered, due to late spring snow melt, on the trail approaching XYZ canyon. Crossing it was slippery and required assistance from all participants.
   - Heavy vehicle traffic on Hwy 1, making caravan process impossible.
   - Snake, scorpion, fire ants, etc., encountered and very apparent around area.
   - Hot weather in excess of 90 degrees throughout day.
   - Fifty or more bees and hornets present at rest stop east of San Clemente Beach.
   - Many deer seen crossing highway on ride back to town at end of day.
9. Summary of Incidents, Near Misses, and Fist Aid Treatments
   Examples:
   - At 10:15 A.M., Bob Smith (participant) was hiking on trail when he slipped on loose rocks and fell to his knees and hands. This resulted in cuts and scrapes to hands and knees. Mr. Smith required first aid from the Safety Watch. His cuts and scrapes were cleaned using sterile materials from the first aid kit, and bandages were applied to the cuts and scrapes.
   - At 9:30 A.M., had a flat tire due to sharp rocks on ranch road east of Sagers Canyon entrance.
   - Oil pan was punctured from hitting high spot in road. Road had many deep ruts from spring runoff of snowmelt.

## Field Activity Safety Process 5B

# Daily Entries in Safety Log Book

*{This outline is to be fastened to the inside cover of the Field Safety Log book}*

**Daily Safety Watch Log:**

1. Date of Entry
2. Name of person making entry
3. Approximate number of participants, to help provide an estimate of exposure hours
4. General location of day's activities, and/or the description of the location where a hazard, unsafe condition, safety observation, near miss, or incidents was encountered
5. Summary of participant-identified "Safety Concerns or Feedback"
   - Details of safety concern, suggestion, etc., including potential hazard and recommended improvements
6. Summary of Hazards, Unsafe Conditions, and Safety Observations:
   - Detailed description/narrative
   - Location, time of day
   - Potential exposure
   - Recommendations to avoid or eliminate hazard
7. Summary of Incidents, Near Misses, and First Aid Treatments that day, with details on:
   - Time of day, what happened, persons involved, actions to respond
   - Cause of event, recommended measures to avoid recurrence

*Designed to be printed front and back on card stock and then trimmed into separate cards*

## Field Activity Safety Process 5C

# Field Safety Card

Emergency Response Actions:

**Activate in case of:**

- ☐ Person injured or ill
- ☐ Separation from group
- ☐ External threat

**Whistle signals:**

— **1 long** blast = ATTENTION
- - - **3 short** blasts = EMERGENCY—activate plan:

***If injured is part of your group:***

1. Remain with injured/ill person
2. Prevent further harm—DO NOT MOVE injured
3. Identify urgent issues: breathing, pulse, severe bleeding

***If injured is not part of your group:***

4. Congregate around Assistant Instructor
5. Await instructions

**Emergency Response Plan responsibilities:**

- ➢ ***Safety Watch*** provides first aid
- ➢ ***Assistant Instructor*** coordinates uninvolved groups
- ➢ ***Lead Instructor*** coordinates response, notification, evacuation, group activities

**Buddy/Group Responsibilities:**

- Watch out for each other
- Early detection of a problem
- Early notification of a problem
- Initial response to injury/illness

Urgent Care basics:

**Check:**

- ☐ Scene (are there additional hazards?)
  - One person takes charge
  - Identify tasks to be performed
  - Approach patient safely
  - Do Emergency Moves **only** if needed
- ☐ Patient (approach safely)
  - Urgent First Aid (breathing, pulse, bleeding)
  - Initial assessment
  - Protect the patient
  - Prioritize care
  - Check for all injuries
- ☐ Resources (people, material)
  - People, Communications
  - Access, Supplies, Transportation

**Call:**

- Plan what to do
- Get help
- Call with essential information
- Send team to meet responders

**Care:**

- Do no further harm; remain calm
- Provide care
- Transport patient if appropriate
- Monitor the patient < every 15 minutes

Emergency Response Actions:

**Activate in case of:**

- ☐ Person injured or ill
- ☐ Separation from group
- ☐ External threat

**Whistle signals:**

— **1 long** blast = ATTENTION
- - - **3 short** blasts = EMERGENCY—activate plan:

***If injured is part of your group:***

1. Remain with injured/ill person
2. Prevent further harm—DO NOT MOVE injured
3. Identify urgent issues: breathing, pulse, severe bleeding

***If injured is not part of your group:***

4. Congregate around Assistant Instructor
5. Await instructions

**Emergency Response Plan responsibilities:**

- ➢ ***Safety Watch*** provides first aid
- ➢ ***Assistant Instructor*** coordinates uninvolved groups
- ➢ ***Lead Instructor*** coordinates response, notification, evacuation, group activities

**Buddy/Group Responsibilities:**

- Watch out for each other
- Early detection of a problem
- Early notification of a problem
- Initial response to injury/illness

Urgent Care basics:

**Check:**

- ☐ Scene (are there additional hazards?)
  - One person takes charge
  - Identify tasks to be performed
  - Approach patient safely
  - Do Emergency Moves **only** if needed
- ☐ Patient (approach safely)
  - Urgent First Aid (breathing, pulse, bleeding)
  - Initial assessment
  - Protect the patient
  - Prioritize care
  - Check for all injuries
- ☐ Resources (people, material)
  - People, Communications
  - Access, Supplies, Transportation

**Call:**

- Plan what to do
- Get help
- Call with essential information
- Send team to meet responders

**Care:**

- Do no further harm; remain calm
- Provide care
- Transport patient if appropriate
- Monitor the patient < every 15 minutes

responsibility is the safety of the Participants and Staff. During group movements and while at potentially hazardous locations the Safety Watch should not engage in technical discussions.

## Key Responsibilities, Normal Operations:

### Lead Instructor/Trip Coordinator/Work Coordinator

- Coordinates overall activity, safety, and emergency response
- Stays out in front of all groups during movements ("on point")
- Coordinates and communicates management of change and revised plans to uninjured participants and staff
- Implements evacuation decision

### Safety Watch

- Maintains safety watch, enforces safety rules
- Carries outcrop safety, communications, and response equipment
- Provides initial first aid
- Stays at rear of group during movements (at "sweep")
- Maintains *Safety Log Book*

### Assistant Instructor*

- Assists with technical training and safe conduct
- Assembles and directs uninvolved class groups in event of emergency
- Stays in the middle of the class during movements

### Logistics Coordinator

- Assists with safe conduct and general health and condition of class
- Issue safety equipment to participants as needed (vests, hard hats, etc.)
- Deploys traffic control devices at roadside stops as required
- Works with Assistant Instructor to manage uninvolved groups during emergency
- Normally remains near parked vehicles for security and as safety watch for participants who may remain in parking area.
- Roles and responsibilities for Field Trips may be similar to above, but not all positions may be applicable.
- When conducting classes with fewer than 17 participants, Lead Instructor may select one participant with appropriate FA/CPR training to perform duties of the Assistant Instructor in case of an emergency.

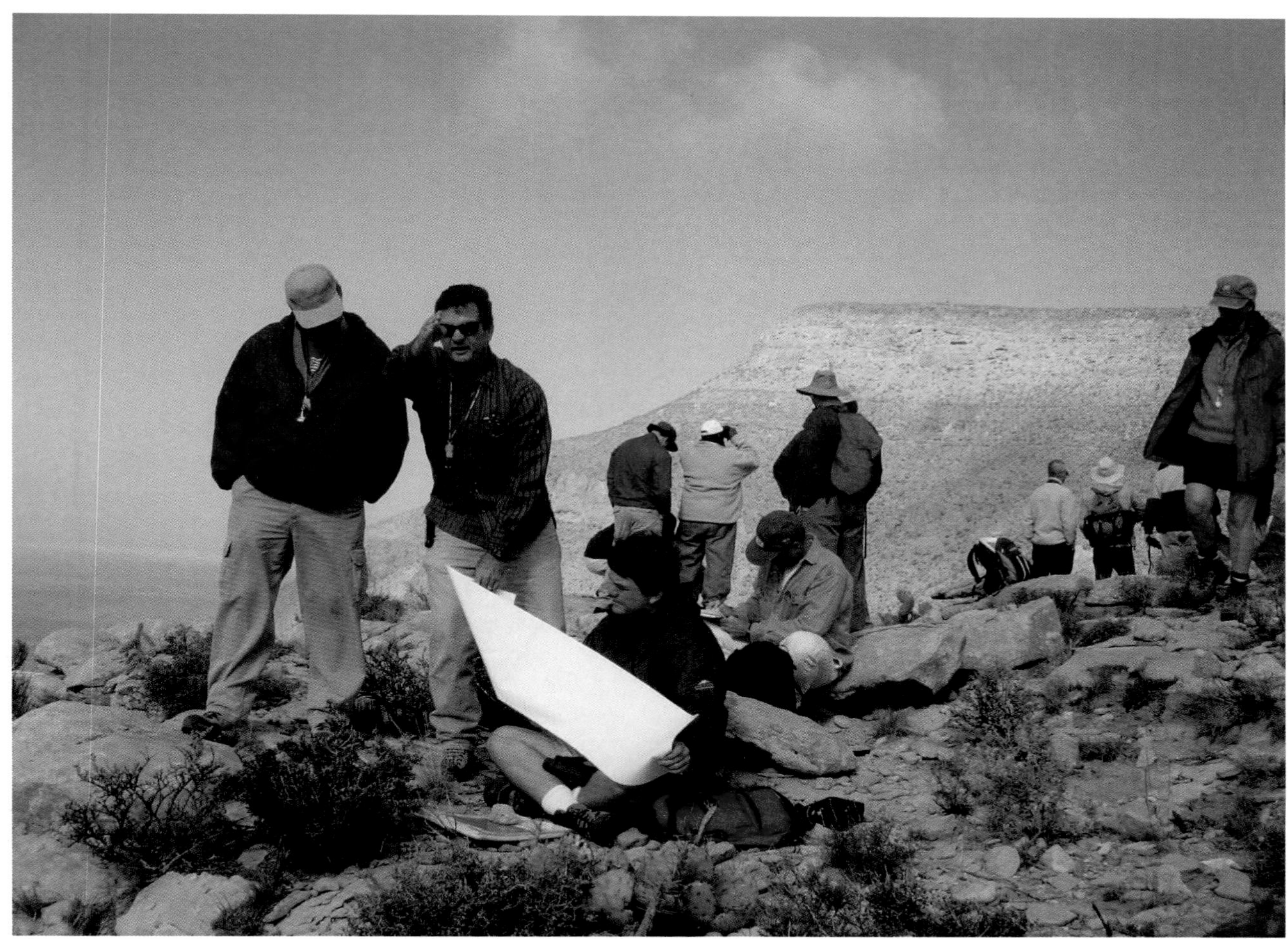

**Key Responsibilities, Emergency Operations:**

Group with Injured Member:

- Activate ERP with whistle
- Remain with/near injured, if safe to do so
- Prevent further harm—DO NOT MOVE injured
- Identify urgent issues: breathing, pulse, severe bleeding

Uninvolved Groups:

- Congregate around Assistant Instructor, if safe to do so
- If not safe to congregate, remain in place
- Await instructions

Assistant Instructor (Middle of Pack):

- Assemble uninvolved groups in a safe place
- Conduct head count
- Stand by to assist, as needed

Safety Watch:

- Acknowledge activation of ERP
- Proceed to location of injured
- Provide initial First Aid
- Assess additional needs
- Request additional resources as needed

Logistics Coordinator:

- Assist Assistant Instructor with uninvolved groups
- Assist with emergency notification and evacuation

Lead Instructor:

- Acknowledge activation of ERP
- Determine severity of situation, in consultation with Safety Watch
- Decide on course of action for patient and uninvolved groups
- Communicate plan to all
- Coordinate treatment, notification, evacuation

### *Alternative Responsibilities/Backup Plans:*

**Lead Instructor injured/ill:**

- Assistant Instructor substitutes for Lead Instructor
- Designate participant substitutes for Assistant Instructor

**Assistant Instructor injured/ill:**

- Designate participant substitutes for Assistant Instructor

**Safety Watch injured/ill:**

- Assistant Instructor becomes Safety Watch
- Designate participant substitutes for Assistant Instructor

## Drivers Briefing

Drivers are selected based on criteria on the ***Guidelines for Driving Organization Vehicles*** form and current certification in defensive driving.

A short briefing will be held with the designated drivers of vehicles. This briefing should cover the following:

- Convoy protocol
- Use of Organization Vehicle Guidelines
  - Accident procedures
  - Alcohol/drugs not allowed
  - Process for reporting any problems with vehicle
- Vehicle Inspection Checklist
- Tire Changing Procedure (includes what the rest of the group is to do if there is a flat tire)

These items are included in the ***Drivers Safety Briefing*** sheet which is kept in each vehicle

## Daily Morning Safety Briefings

Morning safety meetings will generally be held in the hotel or in a safe area near the vehicles at the start of each day. Safety Watch should lead these briefings. They are intended to be short (5 minutes) and should cover the following:

- Brief overview of day's activities: Technical, Logistical, Safety
- Any issues from previous day from Activity Staff (identified in Safety Debriefing) and Participants
- Selected safety topic, relevant to the day's activities
- ERP (roles for the day—see ERP list of roles)
- Reporting of hazards, near misses
- PPE needed that day
- Prompt participants for questions and understanding

## Site Safety Briefing

These briefings will be held upon arrival at each site. The objective is to cover the Site Summary Sheets (reviewing hazards, prevention measures, ERP, group protocol), and to identify any potential changes—anything that is different from normal. The Safety Watch should lead these short briefings (<5 minutes).

### Use of Barriers and Warning Devices

Various types of barriers as listed in the SHE Plan (e.g., cones, flares, flags, etc.) should be used to isolate people from hazards, such as steep cliff, drop-offs, traffic on roads, etc. For example in the event of a flat tire, the vehicle should be pulled off to the side of the road and cones should be place well behind the vehicle, and possibly on the road side of the vehicle.

### Field Safety Log Book

The Field Safety Log Book will be used by the Safety Watch to document items related to safety such as any incidents, near misses, and new hazards. In addition any potential improvements in processes/procedures should be documented as input to the Field Safety Coordinator. See form 5C (above) for guidance and example entries. The book or summary of entries should be provided to the Field Safety Coordinator within 2 weeks of the school/trip completion.

## Standard Operating Procedures (SOPs)–Pre-Trip Water Safety Class Requirements

**Overview:** This school/trip is designed to provide delegates the opportunity to examine modern carbonate depositional environments and modern carbonate sedimentary processes. To fulfill these opportunities it is necessary to use small tourist fishing boats to transit to the localities, and to swim and snorkel in the marine environments. Thus, we will be snorkeling in both protected and open ocean settings. Water depths will range from 1 to 2000 ft (1–610 m). We will experience sea conditions that vary from calm (no waves) to choppy (waves up to 3 ft [1 m]) to open ocean swells. Also, we will snorkel in a tidal channel with a flowing flood or ebb tidal current. These conditions require that each delegate be aware of the water safety issues while participating in any snorkeling activity, and that each delegate responsibly follows the standard operating procedures for these activities.

It is required that each delegate arrives at the field activity with his/her personal snorkel gear or equipment. Equipment must include mask, snorkel, fins, and hard-soled booties. We recommend that delegates needing corrective lenses purchase a mask that has corrective lenses installed. Some individuals can use contact lenses and a snorkel mask, however, there is a chance of losing the lenses in the ocean. Also, we recommend fins with heel straps. We **DO NOT** recommend the step-in, shoe-type fins.

**Water Safety Class and Swimming/Snorkeling Evaluation:** All delegates, instructors, and other staff, who will participate in the modern field portion of the activity, are required to attend a Water Safety Class and to pass a combined swimming and snorkeling test. Anyone who does not attend the water safety class or does not pass the snorkel test will not be allowed to participate in the field activities.

A certified dive instructor will conduct the water safety class and swim/snorkeling test.

**Water Safety Class Overall Objectives:**

1) Enhance personal safety around open ocean water settings through familiarization with common hazards and with safety and snorkeling gear.
2) Evaluate participants' comfort level in water, and evaluate participants' swimming and snorkeling abilities through observation of swim check and practice drills.

**Water Safety Class Learning Objectives:**

1) Participants understand and perform self-rescue skills for water emergencies (proper use of PFDs).
2) Participants understand how to provide assistance to others using non-swimming rescue techniques (reach and throw).
3) Participants understand the use of the buddy system and responsibilities to his/her buddy.
4) Participants become familiar with safe and proper use of snorkel gear (mask, fins, snorkel, PFD) through orientation and in-water practice.
5) Evaluate participants' comfort level and snorkeling abilities through observation of practice session and drills.

**Water Safety Training Class Topics:**

1) Introduction to objectives of training session
   - Why are we here? To learn to be safe and effective in and around the water, so that the technical objectives of the school can be achieved.
   - What's involved?
     - Pre-trip orientation and abilities test in the pool.
     - Multiple water days in the field; 15–45 minute duration snorkel swims; 0.25 to 3 hr boat rides.
2) Introduction of instructor(s)
3) Snorkeling video covers following topics
   - Equipment selection and fitting
   - Entry techniques into the water
   - Mask and snorkel clearing
   - Ascents from depth
   - Environmental conditions (waves, tides, currents, marine life
   - Exits from water
   - Equipment care
   - Buddy system
4) On-Deck pool session: Personal Floatation Device (PFD; life vest)
   - Orientation to Use; where and when to use
   - Practice putting on and taking off
   - Practice inflation and deflation of PFD
5) On-Deck pool session: Buddy System
   - Roles and responsibilities
   - Assign practice buddies
6) On-Deck pool session: Signal communications
   - Hand signals
   - Emergency signals, whistles, airhorn
   - Responses to emergency communications
7) Non-swimming rescues/assists
   - Reaching assists
   - Throwing assists

**Swimming/Snorkeling Test Requirements:**

1) In-Water pool session: Warm-up, Swim Test, and Snorkel Practice and Test
   - Allow participants to acclimate to pool water
   - Allow instructors to assess comfort level of participants in water
2) In-Water pool session: **Certified Instructor Conducts Swim Test**
   The purpose of the swim test is to evaluate the swimming capabilities of each participant, instructor, and other staff members such that the class can be subdivided into three groups, where each group consists of delegates with comparable swimming and snorkeling skills. Three classifications of swimming/snorkeling ability have been defined: advanced (green), intermediate (yellow), and inexperienced (red).

**The swimming test includes:**

- swim 100 yards without stopping
- unassisted treading water for 5 minutes
- unassisted motionless back float for 1 minute
- enter water feet first, turn and return to starting point

**The snorkeling test includes:**

- demonstrate proper use of your PFD or life vest
- demonstrate knowledge of your snorkel equipment
- demonstrate proficient use of your snorkel equipment
  - defog mask
  - clear mask when full of water both at surface and underwater
  - continuous swimming for 100 yards using mask, snorkel, and fins
- demonstrate ability to do feet first water entry with full snorkel gear on
- demonstrate ability to do snorkel surface dive
- demonstrate ability to hear whistle, bullhorn, airhorn while in water with snorkel gear on

3) We will use the following table to score each delegate on the elements of the test.
4) At completion of in-pool tests, the certified dive master will classify each delegate according to ability, and assign each delegate to one of the three snorkel groups that will define instructor and boat assignments during the field phase.

**Water Communication Techniques Orientation:** Following the swim and snorkel tests, the dive instructor will provide instructions for the following signals that will be in use during our field activities.

1) Buddy-to-Buddy hand signals
2) Instructor-to-individual hand signals
3) Instructor-to-group hand signals
4) Safety Watch in boat to participant/instructor in water hand signals

Swim Test Score Card:

| Delegate/Staff | Swim Distance | Tread water time | Float time | Feet-first entry and return | Classification |
|---|---|---|---|---|---|
| | | | | | |
| | | | | | |
| | | | | | |
| | | | | | |
| | | | | | |
| | | | | | |
| | | | | | |

Snorkel Test Score Card

| Delegate/Staff | PFD or Life Vest use | Snorkel equipment knowledge | Defog mask | Clear mask | Swim distance | Feet first entry | Surface dive | Can hear whistle, bullhorn, airhorn | Group Classification |
|---|---|---|---|---|---|---|---|---|---|
| | | | | | | | | | |
| | | | | | | | | | |
| | | | | | | | | | |
| | | | | | | | | | |
| | | | | | | | | | |
| | | | | | | | | | |
| | | | | | | | | | |

5) Safety Watch in boat to participant in water bullhorn verbal instructions
6) Safety Watch in boat to group in water emergency airhorn alerts

**Water First Aid Orientation:** Also, the dive instructor will provide orientation on the following first aid rendering techniques. This does not, however, substitute for the formal field first aid and water safety first aid classes that are required for instructors and for other participants.

1) Cuts, scraps, stings
2) Head/neck injury stabilization
3) Hip and shoulder support
4) Arm splint

### Standard Operating Procedures (SOPs)–Three-Group Swimming/Snorkeling

**Overview:** This school/trip is designed to provide delegates the opportunity to examine modern carbonate depositional environments and modern carbonate sedimentary processes. To fulfill these opportunities it is necessary to use small tourist fishing boats to transit to the localities, and to swim and snorkel in the marine environments. Thus, we will be snorkeling in both protected and open ocean settings. Water depths will range from 1 to 2000 ft (1–610 m). We will experience sea conditions that vary from calm (no waves) to choppy (waves up to 3 ft [1 m]) to open ocean swells. Also, we will snorkel in a tidal channel with a flowing flood or ebb tidal current. These conditions require that each delegate be aware of the water safety issues while participating in any snorkeling activity, and that each delegate responsibly follows the standard operating procedures developed by the instructors for these activities.

It is required that each delegate arrives at the field activity with his/her personal snorkel gear or equipment. Equipment must include mask, snorkel, fins, and hard-soled booties. We recommend that delegates needing corrective lenses purchase a mask that has corrective lenses installed. Some individuals can use contact lenses and a snorkel mask, however, there is a chance of losing the lenses in the ocean. Also, we recommend fins with heel straps. We **DO NOT** recommend the step-in, shoe-type fins.

**Water Safety Class and Swimming/Snorkeling Evaluation:** All delegates, instructors, and other staff, who will participate in the modern field portion of the field activity, are required to attend a Water Safety Class and to pass a combined swimming and snorkeling test. Anyone who does not attend the water safety class or does not pass the snorkel test will not be allowed to participate in the field activities.

A certified dive instructor will conduct the water safety class and swim/snorkeling test. Refer to Pre-Trip Water Safety Class Requirements SOP for test requirements.

**Three-group Categorization:** As a result of the swimming/snorkeling test, each delegate will be classified by swimming/ snorkeling proficiency as:

1) Inexperienced
2) Moderate
3) Advanced

The certified dive instructor will make the determinations.

The class will be divided into 3 groups consisting of a maximum number of 8 snorkelers. Each group will have 1 instructor, a delegate buddy for the instructor, and 3 delegate buddy pairs. We will strive to define the three groups in accordance with the snorkeling proficiency levels, e.g. 1 group of inexperienced snorkelers, 1 group of moderate snorkelers, and 1 group of advanced snorkelers. In the event that the number of delegates with similar proficiency is not evenly distributed, the instructors will confer with the certified dive instructor to sort the delegates into groups, and the category of each group will be based on the lowest proficiency represented in the group.

Once a group has been identified/classified with delegates of like snorkeling proficiency, an instructor will be assigned to that group. The instructor is responsible for all delegates of his/her group.

**Three-group Snorkeling Safety Requirements and Color Scheme:** Commensurate with the snorkeling proficiency level of a group/delegate, requirements have been defined for snorkeling safety.

1) All delegates classified as inexperienced are required to wear life vests, and to have red tape on his/her snorkel.
2) All delegates classified as moderate snorkelers are required to wear life vests, and to have yellow tape on his/her snorkel.
3) All delegates classified as advanced snorkelers are required to wear inflatable PFDs, and to have green tape on his/her snorkel.
4) All instructors are required to wear inflatable PFDs, and to have blue tape on his/her snorkel.

**Three-group Snorkeling Safety Field Practices:**

1) The group rides together in the same boat.
2) The group snorkels together with its instructor.

The instructor provides all technical commentary, observations, and explanations for the stop to his/her group. Buddy pairs must stay with the group. Straying from the group is not acceptable.

3) The group returns to the boat together.
4) The instructor assists delegates' reentry into the boat.
5) The instructor takes headcount, and is last of group to reenter boat.

## Standard Operating Procedures (SOPs)–Road Walking Exposure

1) Orientation provided to delegates prior to departure to the road exposure area.
2) Vehicles are to be parked as far from the active roadway as possible.
3) Delegates are to wear reflective hazard vest prior to exiting the vehicles.
4) Delegates are to exit the vehicles on the side opposite the active roadway.
5) The staff will place road hazard warning signs in front and behind the parking area and where the delegates will be exposed to roadway traffic.
6) The delegates will follow the leader single file while traversing along the active roadway.
7) Always stay as far off of the road as possible.
8) Open-toed shoes are not permitted due to road debries and broken glass.
9) The Safety Watch will be at the end of the group monitoring the safe movement of the delegates and identifying any hazards.
10) If working a roadside outcrop, the Safety Watch will provide group monitoring while the delegates are working along the roadside exposure.

## Change Management during Activity

Sometimes during a particular stop or enroute, conditions are different than expected (weather, people in vicinity, additional hazards, etc.). All Staff and Participants are responsible for identifying changes. If anything is encountered that is **significantly** different than planned, the following process will be used:

- Stop current activity or travel to planned site
- Assemble Group
- Staff confers and decides on plan (including analyzing risks)
- Lead Instructor communicates plan to all participants at one time and checks for understanding
- Proceed with revised Plan

**Deviations from the normal plan must be documented in Safety Log.**

> NOTE: Visiting Alternative Sites that have not been planned or pre-approved is not permitted during Activity. During pre-activity planning, it may be desired to have alternate stops assessed and approved in case a particular stop is not accessible. A Site Summary Sheet is then developed for that alternative site (before the Activity starts). (See In-Field Safety Procedures.)

## Daily Safety Debriefings

At the end of each day, a safety debriefing will be conducted by Safety Watch with the Staff. Any safety issues encountered that day will be discussed, as well as plans for the next day. Specific topics to cover should include:

- Capture lessons for next day briefings
- Assess group functioning and personal interactions
- Assign roles for next day

This debriefing is intended to be relatively short (5 to 10 minutes). After the meeting, the Safety Watch should document key safety lessons and complete the day's entries in the *Safety Log Book*.

## End of Activity Debriefing

Safety will be included as part of the overall Activity written evaluation by the participants and Activity Staff. If time permits, a verbal feedback session should also be held. Items such as near misses, incidents, best practices, and areas for improvement should be discussed and documented in *Safety Log Book*. Capture suggested improvements for both delivering the course and the overall safety process.

# 6 Post-Activity Learning

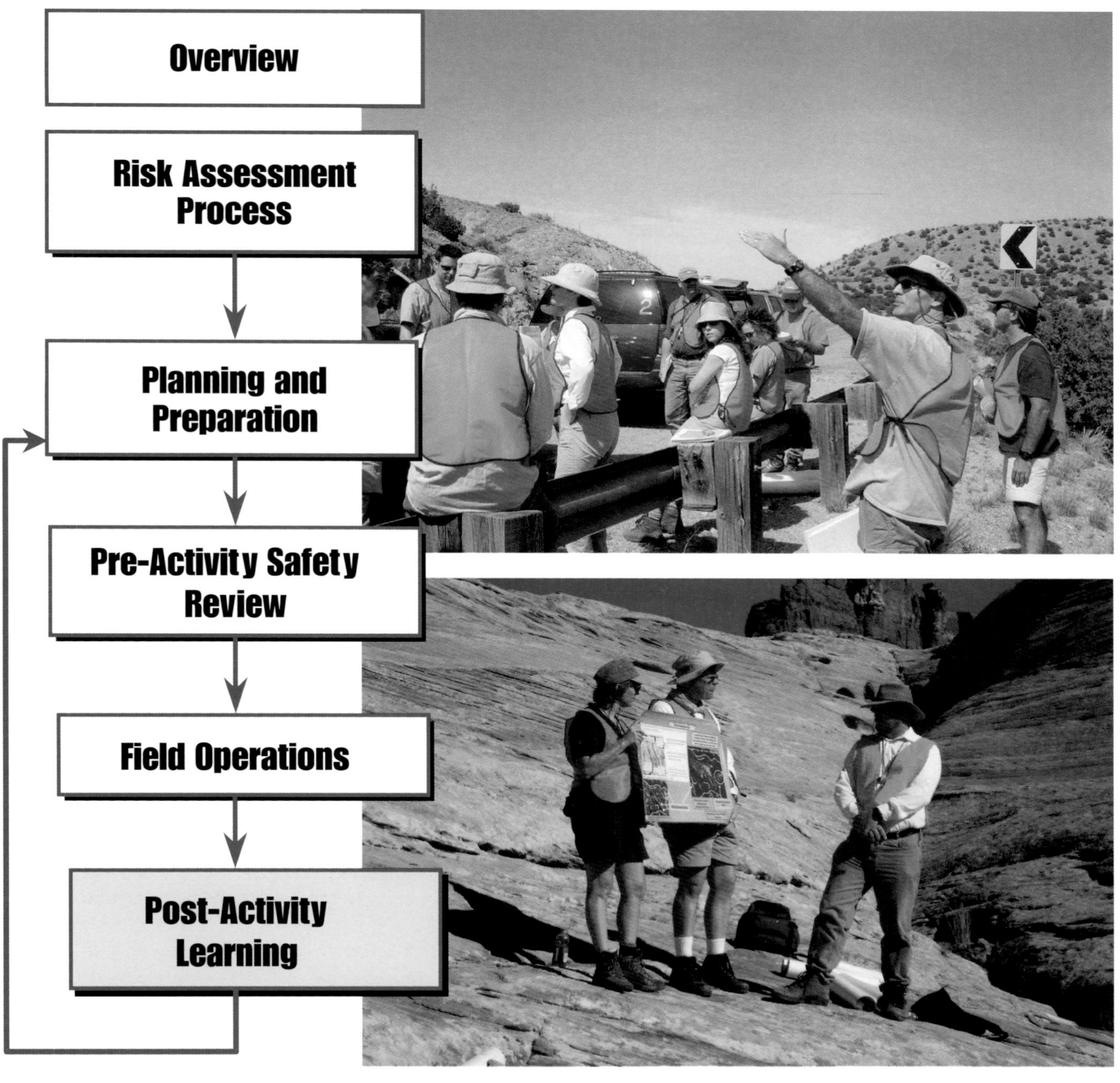

# SECTION 6

## Post-Activity Learning

An important tool for the continued safe and effective execution of all Field Activities is the identification, capture, sharing and incorporation of lessons learned. The Activity Staff will capture information on a daily basis through the daily safety debriefings, Safety Watch log book entries, near-miss reports, etc. The will document lessons learned in the ***Field Activity Follow-up Report*** to be submitted to the Field Safety Coordinator within 2 weeks of the completion of the Activity.

### LESSONS LEARNED DATABASE

At the completion of each Activity, the Activity Coordinator (AC) will review the Follow-up Report and other lessons with the Geoscience Field Safety Coordinator (GFSC) - ideally in a face-to-face session, but by telephone and email when that is not practical. All items will be entered into an "Action-Tracking" database for stewardship, and the GFSC and AC will agree upon follow-up responsibilities as appropriate.

### COMMUNICATING LESSONS LEARNED

As soon as practical (but no later than 4 weeks) after meeting with the Activity Coordinator to discuss safety lessons learned during the Activity, the GFSC will communicate the findings as appropriate to the Staffs and Activity Owners for all Field Activities of the organization.

### QUARTERLY REVIEW WITH STEERING COMMITTEE

The GFSC will meet with the organization's Safety Committee on a quarterly basis to discuss, along with other business, the status of action items in the Lessons Learned Database.

**The following form for this section is also located on the CD-Rom accompanying this book:**
**Activity Follow-up Report Form— 6A**


DOI:10.1306/1119802DEG3223

## Field Activity Safety Process 6A

# Activity Follow-Up Report

Activity: ____________________ Dates: __________

Location(s): ____________________

Activity Coordinator: ____________________ Logistics Coordinator: ____________________

Other Staff: ____________________

**Record pertinent information below. Expand or contract sections as necessary.**

---

**Follow-up Actions on Pre-Activity Issues**

-
-

---

**List (Summarize) Incidents** (Attach actual reports)

-
-

---

**List (Summarize) Near-Miss Reports** (Attach actual reports)

-
-

---

**List (Summarize) Unsafe Act and Unsafe Condition Reports** (Attach actual reports)

-
-

---

**General Safety Learnings and Observations** (Staff-Including Safety Log Book entries)

-
-

---

**Staff Suggestions for Improving Safety on Future Activities**

-
-

---

**Suggestions for Improving Field Safety Process**

-
-

---

**Safety Suggestions/Feedback from Participants**

-
-
-

# References

American Geological Institute, 1992, Planning For Field Safety: 197 p.

Auerbach, P. S., H. Donner, and E. Weiss, 2003, Field Guide to Wilderness Medicine, Second Edition: Philadelphia, Mosby, Inc., 736 p.

Carline, J. D., S. C. MacDonald, and M. J. Lentz, 2002, Mountaineering First Aid, Fourth Edition, A guide to accident response and first aid care: Leicester, England, The Mountaineers, 141 p.

Curtis, R., and Princeton University, 1998, The Backpacker's Field Manual: A comprehensive guide to mastering backcountry skills: New York, Three Rivers Press, 384 p.

National Safety Council and A. L. Thygerson, 1995, First Aid Handbook: Boston/London, Jones and Bartlett Publishers, 192 p.

Nester, T., 2001, Practical Survival: Tips, Tricks, & Skills: Flagstaff, Diamond Creek Press, 40 p.

Reese, C. D., 2001, Accident/Incident Prevention Techniques: London and New York, Taylor & Francis, 552 p.

Smith, D. S., and S. J. Smith, 1994, Water Rescue: Basic skills for emergency responders: St. Louis, Mosby, Inc., 368 p.